CONTE

INTRODUCTION

This booklet was originally called *Curing Eczema* because I believe it is possible to so dramatically improve the health of your skin that you can call it cured.

You have probably tried it all, wasted money on various creams and potions, despaired over yet another failed promise and resigned yourself to a wardrobe full of long sleeved shirts. I have been there and come through the other side.

The difference with this book is that you will learn about yourself and your eczema and personalize the treatment to suit you. As you have probably gathered by now there is no "one size fits all" solution for eczema.

If you have had skin complaints for a long time, be patient with yourself and be prepared to make some sacrifices initially. After thirty-three years of tearing at my entire body, I am free of a skin complaint that robbed me of my serenity, confidence and money. This book is the culmination of my efforts to heal myself and then help others.

MY HISTORY

Initially the eczema started in my elbows, then the backs of my knees until gradually it spread to my arms, face, neck, legs and back. One of the worst times was when my entire face broke out and my eyes swelled shut for a couple of weeks. I looked pretty awful and people on the street would stop and stare. I looked like a skinned tomato. My eczema would go through a repeated pattern of different stages; bleeding, cracked, sticky, infected, and always insanely itchy. It was rare for me to not have eczema somewhere.

CONVENTIONAL THERAPIES

I was just over three years old for my first trip to the dermatologist and I was quite pleased with my giant gold tube of cortisone cream. For the next fifteen years I visited numerous doctors, allergists and dermatologists, each of them giving a sympathetic smile, a little talk about how there is no cure for eczema and a prescription for a stronger steroid cream. I had blissful periods where the new cream would suppress the eczema, only for it to return with a vengeance in a few short weeks.

Eventually the strongest steroid cream available was no longer controlling the eczema and my doctor's only recourse was to put me on systemic steroid pills. I remember crying in resignation as I swallowed the first one, having had the side effects explained to me. I took them for a short time and felt so sick I knew I had to find an alternative.

I was eighteen and the thought of being on steroids for the rest of my life was unimaginable.

DEVELOPING MY OWN APPROACH

I started reading health books, first altering my diet and trying natural creams. Taking control of the situation seemed to help, yet I couldn't stop the flare ups. In University I had a particularly bad time before exams, with the eczema covering most of my body. A year after graduation I started working at a health food store in Michigan, called You Are What You Eat. The owner gave me a hands on education in nutrition, herbs, vitamins, minerals and different methods of healing. I continued to tweak my diet and followed a stringent anti-candida diet for a long time. It helped tremendously but the flare ups kept coming.

While in Michigan I also attended massage therapy classes at night. We had to take an elective class on other healing methods and one of the subjects on offer was homœopathy. As we sold homœopathic remedies in the store and I did not understand how to use them, I took the class out of curiosity.

By the end of that day I was astounded. The system of homœopathy made perfect sense to me and I wanted to know more. I made a mental note that one day I would study it when the opportunity presented itself. For the next few years I worked as a massage therapist. The low point came when stress induced eczema disallowed me from practising for months.

Despite all my efforts to control it, I was still at the mercy of my skin. I had to find a cure or change careers. And so, I moved to London to study homœopathy.

Becoming a Homœopath

One of the requirements of the three year course was to go through homœopathic treatment ourselves. I went to my homœopath regularly whether or not I was suffering with eczema at the time. I found that with consistent treatment my flare ups were happening less often and were generally less aggressive when they did come.

Homœopathy and inherited tendencies

One main difference with homœopathy is the ability to strengthen inherited weakness or susceptibility. Several generations of my family suffered various forms of atopic diseases, mainly eczema, allergies and asthma, so naturally I inherited a tendency towards these problems.

Holistic factors

Additionally homœopathy helped me identify my emotional triggers, which gave me tremendous insight into what causes me stress. It is a wise saying that the body will show what the mind refuses to acknowledge. I believe this is true for most eczema sufferers, and what is happening in your head will affect the integrity of your skin. It is important to realize that finally healing your eczema will take a holistic approach and will encompass mind, body and spirit.

Where I am now

I accept my skin will always be my weak point and if I am under exceptional pressure my skin will show it first. In the past three years I have had about four flare ups. Whereas a flare up in the past would have literally meant skin falling off of large parts of my body, now it consists of a small patch between two of my fingers. If that is the extent of my eczema, call me cured!

WHAT IS ECZEMA?

Eczema falls into a group of problems called atopic diseases, also known as inherited IgE-mediated diseases.

IgE stands for the immunoglobulin E class of antibodies. IgE antibodies bind to special cells in the circulation and when these encounter antigens or allergens, the cells release chemicals that injure surrounding tissue.

An allergen can be anything that stimulates an immune response such as a food, dust, chemicals, pollen or animal dander. Usually these substances are harmless but in the atopic person, an immune response is initiated, leading to allergic reactions.

WHO GETS IT?

Atopic diseases usually run in families and one might find eczema, asthma, hay fever, allergic rhinitis, allergic conjunctivitis and food allergies or intolerances in several members and generations of a family. Some people can move through the diseases, for example, having eczema as a baby, which later disappears only to have been replaced by asthma or hay fever.

WHY AND WHEN DOES IT OCCUR

Aggravating factors can be emotional or environmental or often a combination of both. You may find you experience flare ups when going through an emotional or stressful time in your life. Additionally a flare up can be caused by something in your immediate surroundings, such as contact with irritants like latex, detergent, animals or wool. Perhaps changes in temperature, pollen count or humidity aggravate your eczema, causing it to appear seasonal.

A combination of all of the above makes it seem impossible to find the root cause but I encourage you to take heart and work through it one bit at a time.

DIFFERENT TYPES OF ECZEMA

There are different subclasses of eczema which have clinical names such as seborrhoea, contact dermatitis, atopic dermatitis, nummular dermatitis, generalised exfoliative dermatitis and stasis dermatitis. While naming the eczema might make you feel you have a 'proper' diagnosis, it does little to help the situation.

Using the homœopathic approach, it is the symptoms that are more important than the diagnostic label. Remedies are prescribed for the specific characteristics of your personal eczema.

A) DRY AND SCALING

Generally this is dry skin that becomes itchy in patches, causing scaling as the skin layers heal. Usually this starts in children behind the knees and in the crooks of the elbows or can appear to be cradle cap or diaper rash. At this stage sometimes a natural cream will be enough to provide relief and allow the body to take over natural healing. If the eczema does not respond to a cream, deeper treatment will be needed.

Suspect foods should be tested and eliminated (see page 18), also from the mother's diet if she is breastfeeding. If the person is unable to stop from scratching, the lower layers of skin are torn, and can lead to either bleeding or weeping eczema, or a combination of both.

B) WEEPY

Some eczemas can be weepy or oozing, exuding a sticky, clear or yellow tinted substance. Often this forms into crusts and will adhere to clothing and sheets.

I found that gauze soaked in 100% pure aloe vera juice and then loosely wrapped around the area provided temporary relief, or try one of the herbal infusions from page 15 used in the same way.

c) BLEEDING

Some eczema patches will bleed after scratching and the patch will look red and angry and may be worse for heat or water. This can occur any time but most often in the night when the person is unaware of scratching and has potentially become overheated in bed.

Keep the bedroom cool and consider investing in an air purifier.

d) CRACKED

This is common particularly in the winter, and the cracks can be deep and painful. Often found in the fingertips, in the corners of the mouth and eyes and behind or in the ears.

For deep cracks, a tincture made from the herbs Calendula and Hypericum may help with the pain. Dilute in water and dab on clean skin, or add to a base cream.

e) BLISTERS OR HIVES

Not typically eczema symptoms but can be a precursor to other skin conditions. May be a result of a food allergy.

Aloe vera juice applied externally and taken internally can help.

TOOLS FOR ECZEMA

In this booklet I offer homœopathic remedies, herbal formulas for internal and external use and nutritional advice.

Often a combination is needed and I recommend you keep a record of what you have tried so that you can evaluate your progress. One of the most difficult parts of healing eczema is finding your own personal triggers. Your eczema may become inflamed for no apparent reason, yet if you track it carefully you can start to find a pattern.

Carry a small notebook with you and if you feel your skin start to itch, make a note of what might have started it off. It may be something you ate, a new cream, a different fabric, or it could be an emotional response to something.

Remember that you are unique and your eczema is specific to you and your life. If it feels as though you are groping in the dark the help of an experienced practitioner can be a godsend. If your eczema becomes severely infected you should urgently seek professional advice.

If you have to resort to a short term of antibiotics or steroid creams do not despair. Obviously less is better but you have not ruined everything you are working towards. Stay with it and keep persisting.

USING HOMŒOPATHIC REMEDIES

With homœopathy you choose the remedy that best matches your particular eczema symptoms. If your eczema seems to go through cycles of different stages, simply choose the best 'fit' at the time and if the symptoms change then change the remedy to the one that best covers the characteristics of your eczema at that time.

Choose the remedy that most closely matches your symptoms from the list that follows and take one 6C potency twice a day (one morning and one evening). Consider preparing by taking the *Psorinum* and *Calendula* as described opposite.

How and when to take remedies

Take the remedy away from food, drink and toothpaste, leaving fifteen minutes either side of taking the remedy. Once your symptoms improve significantly and your skin remains clear, stop taking the remedy.

Use the remedy in a 6C potency as described, no matter how tempted you are to jump in with a 'stronger' remedy. Skin complaints need to be treated gently, and the last thing you want to do is aggravate the situation. It may seem as though you are taking an awful lot of remedies but as you heal you will be able to drop the ones you no longer need.

If symptoms later return, repeat the remedy again until you have relief. If the original 6C no longer works, you can try a 30C in the same way, but always start with the 6C first. If you do not experience any improvement after six weeks, or your symptoms worsen, please discontinue and consult a professional homœopath.

Feeling stuck?

Many people have benefited from using the following system but do not give up on homœopathy if these remedies fail to help you.

It is important to realise that these are not the only remedies that can be used for eczema: they are remedies that are most often used for skin complaints, but every person is unique and what may work for one might not be the right thing for another.

This information is the starting point and you may need more support than it can provide. Homeopathy provided the final piece of the eczema puzzle I had been working on for years. If in doubt, call a homœopath near you for help (see the list of Contacts at the back of the book).

Helpful preparation

One remedy I will suggest for all eczema sufferers is **Psorinum 30C**. This remedy helps most skin complaints, particularly when of an allergic or inherited origin. It should also help with the dreaded itching and scratching that leads to tearing the layers of the skin. Put a couple of pills into a large bottle of water and sip it throughout the day. If this remedy isn't helping within three weeks, discontinue and contact a professional.

Additionally in the beginning stages I recommend *Calendula 30C* taken daily to help speed healing. The main aim is to make your skin intact again and heal the damaged layers of tissue.

Once your skin is in one piece again so to speak, keeping it there is much easier.

HOMŒOPATHIC REMEDIES

Sulphur 6C

Known for its affinity to the skin, Sulphur is excellent for eczema that is dry, burning hot and bleeds after being scratched. The patches can look denuded, as though scalded, and the itching can be intolerable, with the person being unable to stop tearing at the skin.

The eczema will be particularly sore after bathing as water aggravates the skin. Heat can also trigger the eczema, particularly on becoming too hot in bed, after exercise, wearing wool next to the skin or in hot weather. The Sulphur patient may want something cool on the eczema for relief but often any sort of pressure sets off the itching.

Graphites 6C

In this case the eczema is oozy, weepy and forming crusts that are sticky with a yellowish tinge. The fluid that weeps may be thin, gluey and seemingly never ceasing. There can also be cracking of the skin, often behind the ears, in the corners of the eyes or mouth, toes, anus, nipples and fingers.

I have often found a Graphites eczema picture to be closely linked to Sulphur and the two can alternate rapidly.

Arsenicum 6C

This remedy has rough and scaly eczema that can burn or swell. The skin may also be terribly dry and look like parchment. The eczema may alternate with hay fever or asthma symptoms producing a thin, watery, burning discharge from the nose and eyes.

Arsenicum patients are typically worse late at night, tend to be very restless, and suffer great mental anguish with the eczema. The pain they feel is of a burning nature that unusually is better from warm water or warm dry applications, (the opposite of Sulphur). They can be very fastidious and impatient, with anxiety and stress triggering a flare up.

Staphysagria 6C

The eczema forms dry thick scabs and can itch violently. An odd characteristic is that when one area is scratched, another starts to itch.

The emotional aspect to this remedy cannot be ignored as it is primarily used after anger or humiliation. The person needing this remedy may feel easily insulted, be very sensitive, and hold in aggression. The eczema can be the body's attempt to release the hostility.

Natrum muriaticum 6C (Nat mur)

Here the eczema tends to be in the folds of the skin and appears red and inflamed. The eczema can also be along the hairline, behind the ears and in the joints such as behind the knees and in the elbows. The lips can be cracked, particularly the lower lip.

A leading indication for the remedy can be an intense craving for salt. People needing this remedy will tend to avoid the heat of the sun, may feel better or worse at the seaside and potentially have a history of suppressed sadness or disappointment.

Rhus toxicodendron 6C (Rhus tox)

This remedy is useful for when the skin is dry, swollen, red and intensely itchy. Tiny prickly blisters can appear and either have clear or pussy liquid in them when squeezed.

There may be a tendency to suffer from stiff sore muscles or joints and lower back pain. Much like Arsenicum, people needing this remedy may find their eczema feels better with heat, especially a very hot bath or shower.

Hepar sulphuris 6C (Hepar sulph)

If your eczema starts to look, feel or smell as though it is becoming infected, add Hepar sulph 6C three times a day along with increasing the Calendula 30C to three times a day. I used to get small pimples along my arms either next to or on top of the eczema patches. Be sure to drink masses of water and get extra sleep.

If you do not see improvement in three days or it becomes much worse, you must see your doctor. You will probably be given antibiotics and steroid creams. That is okay. Use the cream sparingly and then once the infection is gone, come off of it again.

Urtica urens 6C

Typically used for hives, this remedy is excellent when there has been an immediate allergic reaction and the skin starts to swell into raised red blotches. This can very rapidly turn into a patch of eczema so try and calm down the reaction before that happens. This remedy is also very good for allergic responses to bee stings and shellfish.

EMOTIONAL SUPPORT

Very often patients will tell me they start to scratch as a response to an emotional situation, usually from anxiety or a feeling of being out of control. Some people are frightened of confrontation or saying what they really feel and will turn the emotions inwards and scratch instead.

You must become aware of these tendencies and take steps to stopping this behavior. Your skin stands little chance of healing if you are constantly tearing at it because of your fears or worries.

Identify the emotions you have difficulty with and do something about it. Speak to someone, consider seeing a counsellor or other 'talking' therapy, keep a journal, get regular exercise, cry or rage with a friend or in private. You must allow feelings to flow or they will spell trouble for your skin. The following remedies can help support you as you learn to face your fears.

AAA 30C (Triple A)

This is a combination of three remedies that will help you through anxious situations. If you tend to be a worrier, put a couple pills of this in a small bottle of water and sip throughout the day.

Chamomilla 30C

This is excellent for babies who seem to have an eczema breakout with every new tooth. Use three times a day until the tooth has broken through and baby seems calmer.

HERBAL REMEDIES

Herbal remedies can be an invaluable part of a regime to cure eczema. Best results will come from a mixture of 3 or 4 of the most appropriate herbs.

How and when to take herbs

They can be taken as a tea or, more conveniently, as a tincture. Put about five drops of each tincture in a bit of water or juice. Take the mixture three times a day for six weeks, then take a break for two weeks before repeating.

To make an infusion, pour a cupful of boiling water onto a heaped teaspoonful of the herb in a teapot. Steep for five to ten minutes, strain and drink or use as a topical wash.

INTERNAL

Caution

If you are taking any prescribed medication or are pregnant consult a herbalist before taking herbs internally.

Burdock root (Arctium lappa)

Traditionally used as a blood purifier, burdock has excellent detoxifying properties and helps to cleanse the system. It works by enhancing the detoxifying function of the liver. An invaluable part of any herbal mixture for eczema.

Gotu kola (Centella asiatica)

An herb from the Ayurvedic tradition, gotu kola is used as a tonic for the nervous system to relieve stress and tension as well as for healing skin conditions such as eczema. It has excellent antioxidant properties. Use this herb for 6 weeks only then discontinue.

Heartsease (Viola tricolour)

An anti-inflammatory herb. Add to mixture for weeping eczema and also for intolerable itching.

Oregon Grape (Berberis aquafolium)

Very good for chronic skin complaints, Berberis helps to support the skin in general and is of particular help in dry, rough, scaling skin.

Red Clover (Trifolium pratense)

Another excellent blood purifying herb that will help cleanse the lymphatic system. A traditional herb used for clearing many skin problems and especially eczema.

Yellow dock (Rumex crispus)

A general tonic and cleansing herb that is used to treat chronic dry and itchy skin problems such as eczema.

EXTERNAL

Several herbs and essential oils may be used in creams and lotions to soothe the skin and prevent infection. They will not cure eczema but will provide soothing support and can be used as an alternative to hydrocortisone creams while working on a curative programme.

CAUTION

Anyone with eczema should do a patch test before using a new product because an individual reaction is always possible in people with sensitive skin. To do a patch test, apply a small amount of the cream on the inside of the elbow or wrist and wait 24 hours before using on a larger area. This is especially important for products containing essential oils.

Chamomile (Matricaria chamomilla)

The cooled herbal infusion may be used as a lotion to calm and soothe the skin and especially allergic reactions. The calming properties of chamomile essential oil are thought in part to be due to the content of azulene that has marked anti-inflammatory properties. Dilute the oil in a vegetable base, bath oil or lotion before use.

Chickweed (Stellaria media)

The anti-inflammatory properties of this herb will help cool and reduce itching. Make an infusion and cool it to use as a lotion or use Stellaria cream to relieve patches of itchy, dry and red skin.

Lavender (Lavandula Angustifolia)

Soothing, anti-inflammatory and antiseptic, lavender essential oil will help to calm the skin and is especially useful to prevent infection. Dilute the oil in a vegetable base oil or lotion before use or add 3-4 drops to the bath.

Marigold (Calendula officinalis)

An extremely useful herb that is a great healer and is anti bacterial. It promotes tissue healing without infection and may be safely used to heal broken skin. Make an infusion and cool to use as a lotion or compress, or use calendula cream.

Neem

The neem tree has been used in India for over 4000 years and is often referred to as the 'village pharmacy'. In relation to eczema, neem is excellent as it possesses anti-bacterial and anti-inflammatory properties. It can be used as an oil on the skin or is found in creams and lotions. At one point I had seborrhoea of the scalp and found neem shampoo and oil to be the only thing to bring relief.

Aloe

Aloe vera juice is often used for burn victims as it helps promote the healing and rapid regeneration of damaged skin. While growing your own aloe is possible, the juice directly from the leaves is rather gelatinous and can stain, so buy the best quality that you can. When I had the burning 'Sulphur' eczema symptoms, I would apply muslin cloths soaked in cold Aloe vera juice to take out the heat.

Avena or Oats

Take plain porridge oats and place either in a muslin bag or nylon stocking and let the water run through it while preparing a bath. Oats will soften the water, and soothe the skin and are a basic ingredient in many eczema bath oils.

Coconut Oil

Coconut oil is a natural moisturiser and also aids in healing and repairing damaged skin. When my eczema was at its worst, 100% virgin coconut oil was all I could bear to have on it.

Coconuts have a large amount of antioxidants that protect us from damage caused by pollution, stress, poor diet and other aggravating factors. The fatty acids in coconut are also antiseptic, which helps to prevent fungal and bacterial infections.

ADDITIVES TO AVOID

Please trust me when I say I have tried a huge number of the soaps, creams and lotions on the market. I do not use any standard products that can be bought in the pharmacy or supermarket. How can this be? In every case these products contain at least one ingredient anyone with sensitive skin should avoid. Many of them are just a soup of chemicals.

Here is a list of the common additives to avoid:
• Sodium lauryl sulphate and sodium laureth sulphate: this is what makes soap bubbly and it is in pretty much every standard soap product on the shelves. Unfortunately in laboratory tests, it also caused allergies, dandruff and skin irritations. According to the website www.health-report.co.uk "Sodium lauryl sulphate is routinely used in clinical studies deliberately to irritate the skin so that the effects of other substances can be tested." Look for products that say SLS free.
• Mineral oil: this is a mixture of hydrocarbons, obtained from petroleum, which blocks the pores and attracts dirt and toxins to the skin.
• Lanolin: a yellow, semi-solid fatty secretion from sheep's wool. Can cause allergies, especially if someone is sensitive to wool clothing next to the skin.
• Petrolatum: paraffin jelly or petroleum jelly. Much like mineral oil this is not absorbed into the skin and suffocates the pores.
• Synthetic fragrances, colourings and stabilisers. Chemicals, period.
• If alcohol is high on the list of ingredients, it can dry out the skin which will further aggravate eczema.

READ LABELS

Seriously, next time you go to the pharmacy, read the labels of the skin lotions and shampoo bottles. As you have probably gathered by now most of my purchases are made in natural health stores!
There are plenty of wonderful products available that will not aggravate the skin further than it already is.

Rather than buying a huge tub of something that might irritate your skin, systematically test the different products using a patch test on your wrist or elbow.

Most natural health stores have a tester bottle for you to try the product before buying. I would suggest you buy a bunch of small bottles and label them with the name of the cream you are testing.

Only test one cream at a time and write your reactions in your notebook. In a short time you will find the skincare line that works for you. When you do, stick with it.

GENERAL HEALTH

Most complementary therapies look at a person as an individual and do not focus only on the disease to be treated. You are more than your eczema and many times another part of your body is not functioning properly and will also need treatment in order to cure the skin.

Natural toxins need to have properly running channels to leave the body. If the eliminatory systems of the body are over-whelmed, the body will push toxins through the skin in order to keep the internal organs healthy. Often those with eczema will have other complaints such as constipation, lung or liver congestion, chronic kidney problems or general sluggishness. It is very important to sort this out if you want clear skin.

INTERNAL CLEANSING

I continue to do periodic cleansing programs, especially as I work and live in the city. If you have a history of poor diet or substance use, please look into internal cleansing as it may speed up the process of curing your eczema. Clearing up the diet will relieve many overall problems and can be the golden key to rebuilding your skin. As eczema is, at least in part, an allergic reaction it makes sense to take careful stock of your diet to see if something you regularly eat is contributing to your problems.

DIET AND NUTRITION

According to the Merck Manual of Medical Information, the most common foods to cause allergies are milk, wheat, eggs, shellfish, nuts, peanuts, soybeans and chocolate. You may never be diagnosed with a true allergy to these foods, but rather have an intolerance or suffer a reaction to them. Visiting a kinesiologist can be helpful in tracking down a sensitivity.

FINDING OUT WHAT IS IMPORTANT

To suggest that one diet will work for everyone is misleading as each of us will have different triggers. I strongly recommend you make the effort to cut out all possible allergens for at least one month. You will have a better chance of discovering if food sensitivity is a problem for you. Then reintroduce them one at a time as described below.

Those who have followed an anti-candida diet will recognize the basic format of these suggestions. This is not intended to be a permanent diet so please do not be overwhelmed by the strictness of it.

It is highly unlikely you are reactive to every food but these basic guidelines will help you track foods you may be sensitive to.

CHOICE OF FOODS

Where possible, buy organic. If the cost is an issue, then at least make sure anything that you cannot peel is organic. Ideally you would eliminate all sprayed foods as the chemicals simply add to the overall burden on the body.

Another consideration is to eat more raw foods as cooking destroys the natural enzymes that help with digestion. Try to have a couple pieces of fruit and a large salad or crudités daily.

FOODS TO AVOID

For a time all eczema patients should avoid:
- gluten (wheat, rye, oats and barley)
- dairy (all cow's milk, cheese and yoghurt)
- sugar, alcohol and caffeine
- refined foods — processed meats, most convenience foods.
- artificial colourings, flavourings and sugar substitutes.

• anything you cannot pronounce on the label. If you can't say it, do not eat it.

Dairy, gluten and overly processed foods seem to be the main triggers for people with eczema. Soy products have often been highly processed and may or may not be tolerated easily. If you have already eliminated the basic wheat and dairy from your diet and are still having symptoms, you can either continue to test the more common allergens such as nuts and eggs, or you can see a nutritionist or kinesiologist for help.

MAKING THE CHANGE

This diet is a challenge at first but one you can easily overcome with practise and perseverance. It is essential you keep a food diary so that you can record how you feel. If you have a surge of energy, there is a chance your diet was contributing to overall toxicity, and you should stay on this eating plan for a while.

If other complaints such as constipation or excess mucus resolve themselves, something in your diet was to blame and could be contributing to the eczema. In the first couple of days the body can go through a cleansing, meaning that the symptoms you presently have can temporarily become worse or you may get headaches or feel especially tired. Drink plenty of water and get lots of sleep. This will help your body make the changeover.

The reason for going on such a clean diet is to take the strain off your liver and digestive system and allow your immune system to calm down. Often people with eczema will have sensitivities to certain foods, and with atopic diseases, these sensitivities cause the body to go into an inflammatory process. By cutting these foods from your diet you have a chance to heal potential internal damage. Importantly you can reintroduce foods one at a time and evaluate your response to them.

HEALTHY ALTERNATIVES

I know that switching to a less mainstream diet can be difficult. Keep an open mind and try new grains and milk alternatives. I suggest you visit your local health store to do some shopping and read the labels carefully. There are masses of 'free from' cookbooks available for you to experiment with. Here are some alternatives that are readily available:

Flours - rice, corn, soy, potato

Pastas - buckwheat, corn, rice

Milk - rice, and almond if nuts are not a problem

By following the recommendations, you will naturally cleanse your body and will most likely find your skin improves with the better nutrition. If there is a dramatic improvement, it is quite certain you have an intolerance to one of the foods.

FINDING INTOLERANCES

To find the culprit, reintroduce one food at a time and wait three days to see if you have a delayed response. Detail how you feel in your diary.

For example, on the first test day drink a glass of milk and have cheese with lunch. If everything is fine after three days, go on to test the next food.

Four days later, wheat toast for breakfast and pasta for lunch. So long as nothing has changed, keep testing the foods you have avoided thus far.

If you find a specific food causes your energy to drop, your skin to itch, or you feel lethargic or slightly nauseous, avoid this food for a further two months.

Believe me, if you find food sensitivity to be the sole cause of your eczema, you are one of the lucky ones as you have complete control over avoiding the offending food.

SUPPLEMENTS

There are certain supplements I continue to take on a regular basis: Essential fatty acids, digestive enzymes and probiotics. Deficiencies in some of these nutrients are common for people with eczema and initially I would use all of them. As you become stronger you can reduce what you take. Experiment and see what works best for you.

• Essential fatty acids: These are Omega 3 and Omega 6 fats that must be sourced from the diet, and most people with eczema are deficient in one or both of these essential nutrients. An excellent balanced blend of both Omega 3 and 6 can be found in hemp seed oil or flax seed oil (linseed oil), found at good health stores. Use in capsule form or as a free flowing oil, added to your food after it has been cooked (do not cook with it as heat destroys the fatty acids). Keep refrigerated.

- Digestive enzymes: Often people with eczema have low levels of digestive enzymes and the partially digested foods aggravate the gastrointestinal tract. Take as directed.
- Probiotics: These are the friendly bacteria found in the digestive tract and are naturally produced in live yogurt. However, as many of you will be avoiding milk products, look for non-dairy capsules in the refrigerated section of your health store. These are of particular benefit if you have been on antibiotics or any long term medication. Probiotics provide incredible immune system support and will benefit anyone.
- Vitamin B complex: B deficiencies are very common in people with eczema. Find a formula that is yeast free. Check the instructions for use. There are high strength complexes available, but whatever is not used immediately is just excreted in the urine. Thus lower doses taken more frequently may be of more value.
- Zinc: this mineral is essential to the immune system and breaks down the essential fatty acids in the body. As previously discussed, EFAs are often lacking in people with eczema. However, if you are taking EFAs and yet your body is deficient in Zinc, you will not be able to utilize the fats. Start with 30-50mg daily and reduce as you heal.

ADDITIONAL SUPPORT

Some patients have found the following items to be of use when tackling eczema. Try them and see if they make a difference for you.

SUPPLEMENTS

- Aloe vera juice: taken internally twice a day, aloe vera calms inflammation and helps to soothe the gastrointestinal tract. It promotes healthy epithelial tissue and can help to rebalance the digestion if food sensitivities are a problem.
- Vitamin C: This vitamin helps with inflammation and allergic responses. Use a buffered formula so as not to upset the stomach, and take as directed on the label. If you experience loose stools, cut back on the dose.
- Milk thistle capsules or tincture: This herb helps to cleanse and support the liver, which is the main organ of elimination in the body. If the liver is sluggish, the other organs have to try and

pick up the extra work. Supporting the liver helps to break down the various toxins and allergens in the body, easing the burden on the skin.

ENVIRONMENT

- Air purifier: these help to keep the air free from dust, dander, pollen and other airborne allergens which reduces overall stress to the body.
- Washing detergents: I use all 'green' products for washing clothes, dishes, floors etc. The less chemicals in my house the better. You can also find ion balls to use in the laundry rather than detergents.
- Make sure the fabrics you use are gentle on the skin and allow for proper circulation. The skin actually breathes and using synthetic fabrics can stop this action, causing extra heat and possible contact allergy. Long sleeved silk underwear is a good choice to have next to the skin as it gives comfort and protection. Otherwise soft cotton is fine.
- Buy cotton gloves to help keep your hands clean after putting on your creams but also to provide extra protection. Wash them frequently.

OTHERS

- Bach Flower rescue formula: In consultations I notice people often start to scratch their eczema when talking about mental or emotional stress. This product is a blend of flower essences that helps calm and comfort when under emotional pressure.
- If vigorous exercise causes your skin to flare, drop the intensity but make sure you do something daily. Walking, yoga and rebounding on a mini trampoline are all good forms of exercise that do not require you get in a lather. Swimming in chlorinated pools can aggravate skin complaints so look for an ozone treated pool in your area.
- Don't forget about cosmetics. These are usually laden with chemicals so look for a natural line (see suppliers at the back of this booklet).

HOMŒOPATHIC CASES

I t can be helpful to read through other people's cases so that you can gain an understanding of what a homœopath would look for in a consultation.

As you can see, each person is different although all suffer from the same complaint of eczema.

CASE ONE

(After 9 months of treatment patient reports 80% improvement of eczema).

"Homœopathy has worked wonderfully for me. Having tried many remedies to relieve my eczema, it has truly been the only thing that has worked. It is also a comfort to know that homœopathy treats your body and your self with respect."

Ms. M, age 25

PRESENTING COMPLAINT: ECZEMA

Ms. M first had eczema at the age of four, with patches on the backs of her knees. In the past three years, the eczema has spread to her face, neck, arms, hands, legs and stomach.

ECZEMA SYMPTOMS

Very dry, red, sore and blotchy on her face, worse around her eyes and mouth. Deep cracks in the corners of the mouth and the eyebrows. Very itchy, worse for becoming hot in bed and after bathing. She scratches until it bleeds.

DIET

Loves sweets such as cakes and puddings, carbs such as bread and potatoes. Likes cheese and milk, fruit and vegetables. Does not like fish or salt. Drinks 2 litres of water a day. 5 cups of tea daily, little bit of wine.

MEDICATION

History of cortisone creams.

ALLERGIES

Feathers and hay fever.

GENERAL INFORMATION

She likes the heat as she is a chilly person even though her eczema feels hot.

She has some insomnia, wakes up scratching, which could be because the bedroom is hot. Energy drops from 3-5:30pm.

FAMILY MEDICAL HISTORY

Ms M's mother has coeliac disease which is a gluten allergy, and her father died at age 42 from cancer. Cancer and diabetes run in the grandparents' history.

EMOTIONAL HEALTH

Ms M becomes wounded easily but will not show anyone except her boyfriend. Not even her mother knows when she is upset. She has a hard time standing up for herself and cannot disagree with people.

She has been a people pleaser since a small girl and was shy, very conscientious, self driven and a perfectionist. At the age of eight, she had to take an entire year off school because she made herself so worried about her friends, who were constantly arguing. She cannot handle confrontation in any form and becomes stressed very easily.

Her eczema flared badly at age 16 when her father became ill. He died two years later and she doesn't feel as though she properly grieved. She suppresses her emotions and will not share her feelings with her friends because she does not want to burden them. She cries on her own or does not cry at all, holding it in.

She worries about what other people think of her and fears she will not achieve enough in her life. She can become despairing and then scratches at her eczema because she does not care anymore.

HOMŒOPATHIC EVALUATION

Ms M has a tendency to hold in her emotions, become terribly stressed, and then tear at the eczema. She needed remedies for the emotions plus the eczema symptoms.

Over the past nine months of treatment, she has received three remedies continually, increasing gradually in potency as she strengthens. There have been other remedies dotted in as needed but primarily she has done very well on the three.

One of these remedies covers the history of grief, tendency to hold in the emotions, fear of confrontation and family history of cancer.

The second is helpful for a chilly person with eczema, intolerable itching, allergies and anxiety about the future.

Finally I gave her a specific remedy for eczema that is worse in the heat, after bathing, and bleeds when scratched.

She was also given a cream to use that contained herbal remedies.

PROGRESS

She has steadily improved despite some very challenging circumstances. As is normal she has had some flare ups. However, the eczema is not as severe, nor does it cover as much skin surface as it used to. She can bring it under control quickly now with the remedies.

Perhaps more importantly she is starting to stand up for herself, speak her mind, and even negotiated a long deserved salary increase. She recently broke up with her boyfriend, the only person in the past she had felt safe with, and her skin did not flare.

CASE TWO

Baby A, male, 8 mths old. (2 months of treatment)

ECZEMA SYMPTOMS

At birth, A's legs were very scaly and he had huge milk crusts on his scalp. His eczema started at age 2 months and has spread to his face, chest and arms. His legs are still the worst.

His skin is very dry and itches terribly. His mother keeps him in long sleeves and socks as he scratches until he bleeds if left unclothed.

GENERAL INFORMATION

He is a happy baby, eats like a horse, loves everything and sleeps through the night. In all respects he is healthy and contented, except for his skin complaint.

Baby A also had a chest infection in the winter, and continues to sound as though there is mucus in his chest.

FAMILY MEDICAL HISTORY
His mother suffers from eczema and his father has hay fever. Allergies run in the family up to the grandparents.

MEDICATION
He was on heavy steroids, which suppressed the eczema. As soon as they discontinued the creams, the eczema came back with a vengeance according to his mother.

HOMŒOPATHIC EVALUATION
The first prescription focussed heavily on the family tendency to atopic disease, as he had skin complaints from birth. This suggests hereditary weakness rather than a dietary or environmental cause.

He was given two different remedies, one for the family history and one for the specific characteristics of the eczema. He was also given a cream with herbal remedies.

PROGRESS
In his follow up appointment his mother said that his eczema overall is better as his face, chest and arms are down to small patches, but that his legs were still bad. This is in the order I would expect. As the legs were the first to show the eczema, there is a good chance they will be the last part to heal.

He was given the same remedies in a slightly stronger potency, and I added another remedy that covers both eczema, allergies and chest complaints.

I anticipate Baby A will be free of eczema after another couple of treatments.

CASE THREE   *(After 18 months treatment patient reports 75% improvement in eczema).*

"During 2003 I suffered from two major attacks of a virulent rash which covered great parts of my body, arms, legs and, worst of all, around my eyes, where the skin alternately burned or irritated. The first attack at the beginning of the year lasted three months and the second in the summer another two months.

Since taking the homœopathic remedies prescribed by Adrianna Holman my skin has been totally clear — this despite the fact that I have had to cope with quite a deal of stress during this time and stress had been diagnosed as the major cause of my skin problems. I am very grateful to Adrianna and her knowledge and experience of homœopathy."

Mrs. F, age 78

MEDICATION

Mrs F had tried adjusting her diet excluding wheat, dairy and alcohol. Her complaint started fifteen years ago after taking pills for weight loss. Her GP told her that her problem was allergies and put her on steroids. The rash subsided but she felt terrible and bloated, so she discontinued treatment.

ECZEMA SYMPTOMS

When she first came to see me her entire face, neck, arms and torso were in a burning painful rash. Her eyes watered continuously and she was distraught with her skin. There is no family history of allergies.

EMOTIONAL HEALTH

Mrs F is anxious about many areas of her life, stating she is incredibly fastidious and becomes hysterical with worry. I gave her a remedy for the burning and itching in addition to treating the anxiety. Her skin started showing signs of improvement almost immediately as did her fears.

UPS AND DOWNS

A couple of months later she had a shock with her daughter and broke out with eczema. She had a different sensation of stinging rather than burning around the eyes. This indicated she needed a different remedy, which fortunately worked quickly.

She was fine for about three months and then another flare. Again there was an emotional cause, mostly anxiety. We went back to the first remedy and it was successful. Mrs F has now determined that she is definitely worse for eating wheat and dairy as it affects her digestion as well as her skin. Cutting those foods from her diet has helped her health overall.

Recently during the summer in the hot weather she wore a polyester top and broke out. We think it may be because her skin cannot breathe through the fabric and I suggested natural fibres during the summer. She is now confident with using the remedies for acute flare ups but still checks in with me regularly.

PROGRESS

Mrs. F has been in treatment with me for 18 months, and we have been able to stretch her appointments to where she sees me every eight weeks rather than the once a month initially.

While she is still getting eczema every once in a while, she tells me that homœopathy has definitely cut down the frequency and severity of the attacks. She has also taken positive steps to addressing her stress and rarely speaks of her previous worries in the consultation.

FINAL WORDS

The emotional pain associated with eczema cannot be ignored. I used to feel I was alone, cursed with an ugly disease that caused me to hide away from society. I was ashamed of my appearance and hated feeling so unsightly.

As much as you may find your skin horrible, treat yourself with love and compassion. You will overcome this by taking the time to truly understand yourself and learn what is best for you.

Curing eczema is a process and not immediate magic. If it were as simple as 'one size fits all' there would be no need for this booklet. Making positive changes with your diet, reducing stress and using the homœopathic and herbal remedies will move you towards cure.

WHAT TO EXPECT

The million dollar question is "How long will it take?" A very rough guide is to give one month of treatment for each year you have had the complaint. Do not despair! What this means is that as you work at curing your eczema, the flare ups will come less often and you will have the means to control them faster.

In the beginning of treatment it can seem to get worse, especially if you have decided to come off of steroid creams. Keep at it and find your triggers. Eventually you will forget you have a skin condition and a flare up will bring your attention to something that occasionally needs addressing.

Have faith that you can cure your eczema. This approach has helped many people and I hope it will help you too.

CONTACTS

To find a practitioner near you contact your local Neal's Yard Remedies Therapy Rooms (see opposite) or contact the following organisations:

HOMŒOPATHY

The Society of Homeopaths
11 Brookfield,
Duncan Close,
Moulton Park,
Northampton
NN3 6WL
Tel: 0845 450 6611
www.homeopathy-soh.org

Alliance of Registered Homeopaths
Millbrook,
Millbrook Hill,
Nutley,
East Sussex
TN22 3PJ
Tel: 08700 736339
www.a-r-h.org

HERBALISM

The National Institute of Medical Herbalists
56 Longbrook Street,
Exeter,
Devon
EX4 6AH
Tel: 01392 426022
www.nimh.org.uk

NUTRITION

British Association for Nutritional Therapy (BANT)
27 Old Gloucester Street,
London
WC1N 3XX
Tel: 0870 606 1284
www.bant.org.uk

SUPPLIERS

NEAL'S YARD REMEDIES

To find your nearest shop or Therapy Rooms:
telephone: 01747 834634 OR
www.nealsyardremedies.com

Mail order tel: 0845 262 3145 OR
www.nealsyardremedies.com

- Natural therapists
- Simple base creams and lotions to add your own blend of herbal tinctures or infusions.
- Herbs, supplements, homœopathic remedies and natural skin care.

AINSWORTH'S HOMŒOPATHIC PHARMACY

36 New Cavendish Street,
London
W1G 8UF
Tel: 020 7935 5330
www.ainsworths.com
Helios Homœopathy

HELIOS HOMŒOPATHY

89-97 Camden Road,
Tunbridge Wells,
Kent
TN1 2QR
www.helios.co.uk
Tel: 01892 537254

THE AUTHOR

Adrianna trained on the full time course with the College of Homœopathy in London and gained her registered status with the Society of Homeopaths shortly thereafter. She has completed further studies in toxicology and homœopathic methodology and treats a wide range of complaints, not just eczema!

Managing a health store in the US for two years provided her with a solid grounding in nutrition and natural therapies. She has ten years experience as a massage therapist and is presently working towards her second Bachelor of Science, specifically focused on Nutritional Medicine.

Adrianna runs her homœopathic practice from several clinics in London, including an Eczema Clinic at Neal's Yard Remedies Therapy Rooms, 6 Northcote Road, Clapham Junction SW11 1NT (020 7223 7171).

She also offers phone and online consultations for people outside of London. She publishes a free online newsletter giving tips and advice on overall health. All feedback and testimonials are warmly welcomed as it helps her continue to learn and help people with eczema.

To contact Adrianna:
  phone 0845 230 0474   OR
  e-mail help@homeopath-online.com
  She has two websites: www.homeopath-online.com
        and   www.homeopath.moonfruit.com
                    (for broadband with Flash enabled browser)

An Unlikely Rebel

Robert Kett and the Norfolk Rising, 1549

by Adrian Hoare

'Never shall I be found wanting where
your good is concerned' (Robert Kett)

Drawings and maps by Anne Hoare

Also by Adrian Hoare
    In Search of Robert Kett
    On The Trail of Robert Kett of Wymondham
    Standing up to Hitler

ISBN   0 900616 55 5

Further copies can be obtained from the author c/o Geo. R. Reeve Ltd.

Front cover: By permission of The British Library, from 'Admirable Curiosities'
        by R. Burton, published in 1682. Shelf mark 600. C38

Printed and published by
Geo. R. Reeve Ltd., 9-11 Town Green, Wymondham, Norfolk, NR18 0BD.

Sworn statements made before the Mayor and Aldermen of Norwich 1550- 1551

'I did well in keeping Kett's camp and thought nothing but well of Kett. He trusted to see a new day, for such as I.' (1550)

'T'was a merry world, when we were yonder eating mutton'. (1550)

'Such as were slain and dead upon Mousehold in the Commotion time were honest men, and Kett was an honest man'. (1551)

ACKNOWLEDGEMENTS

I am indebted to all those who have written about Tudor England and Kett in particular; a select bibliography appears on page 80. The quotations in the text which are not given a source, are from Sotherton's 'The Commoyson in Norfolk' and Neville's 'Norfolk Furies', two near-contemporary accounts of the rebellion.

The staff of Wymondham Library have been cheerfully obliging during my research, for which I am grateful; I also acknowledge the help and advice given by the staff of the Norfolk Record Office and for permission to refer to original documents held there. The reference numbers are: NCR Case 26b/59, PD 254/171, NCR Case 18a/7 and PD 209/479. The Norfolk Studies Library has also been a mine of information and its staff very helpful. Many people too numerous to mention have assisted me, often unknowingly, in a variety of ways, and this has been much appreciated. However, I am especially grateful to the following for their help: Janet Smith, Sheila Spicer, Paul Cattermole, David Cross, David Mawson and Jonathan Hoare. Elizabeth Rutledge has kindly allowed me to make use of the results of research she directed with Fiona Macdonald, for a Cambridge University Extra-mural class in 1984.

At Geo. R. Reeve Ltd., Brian Seager, Tim Smith and Ray Woolston have been very helpful and efficient.

Finally I would like to thank my wife for her encouragement and support, her endless patience in preparing the maps and drawings and for the countless other ways in which she has helped in the preparation of this book.

CONTENTS

INTRODUCTION

The 450th anniversary of Kett's Rebellion is a good time to retell the story of one of the most exciting episodes in Norfolk's history. Robert Kett, Wymondham's greatest son, is not only a Norfolk hero but also a figure of enduring national interest. For six weeks in the summer of 1549, he gave a voice to the lower orders of society, at a time when there was no other way for them to express their views except by protest or demonstration. His impact was felt not only in Norfolk, but also by the government in London.

On 7 December 1549, the Wymondham tanner was hanged as 'a felonious and malicious traitor' and for more than 300 years this verdict remained unchallenged. The early accounts of the rebellion were hostile, representing the views of the victors and based on the biased near-contemporary accounts of Sotherton (c1560), Neville (1575) and Hollinshed's Chronicles (1578), none of whom displayed much sympathy for the rebels. Not until the Reverend F.W. Russell's 'Kett's Rebellion in Norfolk' appeared in 1859, was Kett seen in a more favourable light and as deserving a better fate. Russell was also the first to reject the description of the rebels as 'vile rabble', and praise their bold spirit of resistance to oppression. Our century has seen Kett portrayed even more sympathetically and in proper historical perspective. In 1949 the citizens of Norwich placed a commemorative plaque on Norwich Castle where 400 years earlier Kett had been hanged. He is described as a 'notable and courageous leader', a healthy corrective to earlier judgments, for though Kett had Norwich at his mercy, the city was not destroyed nor were its citizens murdered or raped.

Little documentary evidence has survived about Kett the man, but much can be revealed about him from a study of what he did, especially in the summer of 1549. His world is remote from ours, yet his aspirations for a more just society, his moderation and rejection of violence, and above all his courage, are testimony to an outstanding character.

Once Kett's camp was established on Mousehold Heath, Norwich became politically the centre of interest of the whole country; for much of the summer of 1549 the government was in 'great perplexity' about Kett's rebellion.

Foreign envoys also became very concerned about the situation. In July the Imperial ambassador informed the Emperor Charles V of the spread of general unrest, and that over 8,000 rebels had gathered in Norfolk. In the ensuing weeks the Emperor was kept fully informed about the Norfolk Rising. After initial attempts to suppress Kett failed, the ambassador became concerned that a company of 400 cavalry which the Emperor had hired out to his English ally to deal with the Scots, would be used against Kett's followers instead, thereby creating anti-foreign feeling. The rebels were certainly enraged by the government's use of foreign troops against them and in the final battle, mercenaries from Germany, Italy, Switzerland and the Netherlands made an important contribution to the government's victory.

Kett and the thousands who followed him lost their lives in a cause they believed was just. However, no rebellion which had human rights among its motives can be dismissed as futile or condemned because it was declared illegal at the time. We owe our rights and liberties to that brave band, who down the centuries have struggled against injustice, oppression and greed, in the pursuit of freedom and the establishment of just conditions. Kett has an honoured place in such company. He deserved a better fate than the one he was condemned to on that cold December day 450 years ago. This book is a tribute to him and all his followers.

BACKGROUND TO REBELLION

A time of turmoil, disorder and unrest

For many years before the dramatic summer of 1549, there had been increasing unrest in East Anglia and elsewhere, usually in the form of riots against enclosure of common land. This practice involved the local landowner fencing off part of the common land, for his private use and profit. Common land was traditionally shared by all the villagers who depended on it for grazing their livestock.

In Norfolk, there were enclosure riots at Fakenham in 1520 and in 1525, similar disturbances occurred at Lavenham in Suffolk. At Walsingham in 1537, men conspired to organise a rising as a protest against local injustice. However, the plot was discovered, quickly suppressed and its leaders executed. One man was recorded as saying that, 'It was a good dede that the Comynalte (common people) should rise here as they did in Yorkshire', a reference to the rebellion in 1536 known as the Pilgrimage of Grace led by Robert Aske.

A decade of disorder preceded the Norfolk Rising of 1549. At Hingham in 1539, there were riots in protest against Sir Henry Parker who had enclosed part of the commons.

However, it was perhaps at Griston in 1540, where the temper of the common people was first expressed with real vehemence. John Walker said, 'It were a good thing if there were so many

Hingham

8

gentlemen in Norfolk as there be white bulls'. This outspoken man seems to have wanted to raise West Norfolk in rebellion by the ringing of church bells, to kill gentlemen, to take King's Lynn and 'spoyle' the big men of the area. He claimed 10,000 were ready to rise at Swaffham, but it is one thing to express strong feelings and have big ambitions, and quite another to make things happen.

There were more disturbances at Great Dunham in 1544 and 'talk' of risings among the poor at Buckenham, Fincham and Swaffham. Four years later in 1548, further rioting broke out at Great Yarmouth, Middleton and King's Lynn. John Chaundeler, a parson from Ailthorpe said, 'I would the town of Lynn and all the gentlemen there were on fyre'. His dislike of the gentry was probably based on the allegation that their servants had been killing poor men while they worked in the fields.

But although the 'temper' of Norfolk led to mounting unrest in the 1540s and much 'talk' of rebellion, many men recognised that they needed a 'bold felowe' to lead them. It is significant that the most challenging protest for the authorities, was the one which began in Wymondham in 1549 under the outstanding leadership of Robert Kett.

King's Lynn Guidhall

1549 - A summer of trouble

During the spring and summer of 1549, there was widespread unrest in southern England. In May, rioting occurred in the western counties and the south east, which soon spread into East Anglia. In Norfolk, the villagers of Wilby, Eccles and Attleborough, enraged by the actions of a local landowner John Green, who had enclosed part of the common land in Attleborough and Hargham, pulled down his fences.

Meanwhile a major revolt had broken out in Devon and Cornwall. By early July, disorder had spread to many of the midland counties too. Few parts of southern England escaped the wrath of the 'poore commons' in that fateful summer of 1549.

9

The causes of unrest

The first half of the 16th century was a period of great upheaval with huge economic and social changes. A people wedded to the traditional round of customary tasks in a self-sufficient economy dependent on common rights, now faced the unpredictable storms of a market economy in its early and difficult stages.

When the monasteries were destroyed in the 1530s, much monastic land came on to the market. This was snapped up by ambitious members of the gentry, who were keen to exploit the ever increasing demand for wool, by expanding their sheep farming. Consequently some of the rich became very wealthy, while many of the poor became paupers. The gap between the landowners and the peasantry widened dangerously. In 1500 the Venetian envoy had written, 'The common people are held in little more esteem than if they were slaves'. Dislike of the gentry by the poor, grew into hatred. The Duke of Somerset, uncle of the boy king Edward VI and Protector of England (1547-49) recognised this trend when he wrote, 'All have conceived a wonderful hate against gentlemen and taketh them as their enemies'.

'Pluck down Enclosures'

At a time when the demand for wool both at home and abroad was increasing, the enclosure of land for sheep farming became a major feature of the Norfolk countryside. At the same time protests against enclosure became louder and more vigorous.

There were probably three sheep to every person in early Tudor England and the following contemporary rhyme must have had real meaning for many of the poor of Norfolk.

Monastery remains at Wymondham

10

Sheep at Hargham

'*Sheep have eaten up our meadows and our downs, our corn, our woods, whole villages and towns*'.

Sheep farming also meant fewer jobs:

'*Houses where pleasure once did abound nought but a dog and shepherd is found*'.

There were three types of enclosure, of waste, arable strips and commons, but invariably the process caused hardship to many. For years, enlightened thinkers had said that enclosure led to the poor losing their livelihood and the rich getting richer. The issue of common right of pasture became the main battleground between the small farmers who valued it for grazing their livestock and obtaining manure for their arable fields, and the big landowners or gentry who favoured enclosing as much land as they could for sheep farming.

However, enclosure was not necessarily illegal in many cases, because the common pasture was the property of the lord of the manor, provided he left enough to satisfy the common rights of freehold tenants. But the law was hardly just, as many tenants at this time did not enjoy the privileges of freehold, and there was no protection for their common and customary rights. In any case, the disappearance of common pasture was bound to cause anger, whatever the law said. Enclosure therefore, became a major grievance which affected every man, woman and child in every village where a common was enclosed.

During Henry VIII's reign (1509-47), Cardinal Wolsey's attempts in 1515-17 to check enclosure failed, because the influence of the landed gentry who favoured it was too great.

11

Consequently, much common land in Norfolk disappeared in these years. Furthermore, the traditional rights of the poor to collect timber from the woodlands, to hunt in the forests and fish in the rivers was also being eroded. Some areas were more fortunate than others, for example Old Buckenham, where even today there still remains a large common.

As we have seen, rioting and pulling down fences became more frequent in 1549, but in Wymondham it was the spark which would lead to a much bigger and broader-based rebellion.

Incidentally, surviving documentary evidence held in the Norfolk Record Office (ref: PD 254/171) indicates that during the rebellion, Buckenham Castle was plundered by local rebels from New Buckenham and Carleton Rode, who also killed a deer in Buckenham Park. The local gentleman, Sir Edmund Knyvett was targetted because he tried to disperse a rebel 'camp' at Hingham before it moved on to Kett's Camp on Mousehold.

High prices and high rents

Although enclosure was a major grievance, there were other causes of the unrest in Norfolk. Prices had risen dramatically between 1500 and 1549; since 1530 they had gone up by 30%. The debasement of the coinage by Henry VIII and Protector Somerset fuelled the flames of inflation and also increased the demand for English exported cloth. This encouraged a more entrepreneurial and capitalistic approach to wool production by the gentry, who accumulated as much land as they could to convert into sheep pastures thereby increasing unemployment. By the 1540s when many families were falling on bad times, there was no support service for them now that the monasteries had gone. Higher rents increased the hardship of the poor, many of whom were evicted from their cottages. The relationship between the landlords and their tenants worsened.

'A conspiracy of rich men'

By the mid 1540s, class feeling had become intense as the common people came to regard the greed of their social superiors as the chief cause of their distress. Sir Thomas More's judgment of the landowners in the 1530s as, 'a conspiracy of rich men seeking their commodities', would have seemed to the lower orders, an apt description of the Norfolk gentry in the 1540s. Certainly hatred of the gentry acted as a unifying bond in the story of Kett's Rebellion. Newly erected fences and hedges became for the poor, the symbols of a selfish and greedy class.

A new King and new hopes

The acession of the nine year old Edward VI to the throne in 1547 raised hopes that this was the dawn of a new age, particularly as real power rested with the King's uncle, Protector Somerset, known as the 'good duke'.

Somerset was dutiful, industrious, devout, humane and by contemporary standards, enlightened. His reputation as the 'good duke' was based on the popular belief that he was the champion of the poor and oppressed against the rich. He turned his back on the harsh treason and heresy laws of Henry VIII's reign, and revived the Court of Requests to hear poor men's causes. More significantly, he set up the Enclosure Commission, a body to investigate enclosure and check its worst abuses.

John Hales, Somerset's chief adviser on enclosure was confident that the Protector had a real concern for the general good. He wrote, 'The people perceive your Grace's great zeal and love toward them. The people have a great hope that the Iron world is now at an end and the Golden is returning again'. Those who had criticised landlords as 'men without conscience', or like Bishop Lattimer, held them responsible for the increase in beggars, welcomed the hopeful mood of the new reign.

False hopes and increased hardship

However, hopes of better times for the poor were soon dashed. Far from becoming a period of calm and quiet prosperity, the reign of Edward VI became the most troubled of the Tudor age. Storm clouds quickly gathered as inflation led to soaring prices and rents. War against Scotland and France brought increased taxation, while the Protestant Reformation eroded traditional certainties and encouraged a belief in social egalitarianism. Somerset's Enclosure Commission set up in 1548 and the new sheep tax, achieved little because of the power of the gentry and the opposition of powerful rivals in the royal council, notably the ambitious Earl of Warwick. Even so, Somerset denounced enclosure in a proclamation (May 1549), and said that landlords would be made to toe the line. But it was too late and across southern England the peasantry erupted in revolt.

The Government begins to restore order (1549)

Somerset soon realised he would have to use force, but in an attempt to avoid this he promised a general pardon to all fence breakers on 14 June. This had the opposite effect and in Attleborough a week later, fences were pulled down by an angry mob, during the riots to which reference has already been made.

With serious unrest spreading, on 8 July Somerset ordered local gentry and officials to suppress the disturbances. This was the very weekend that Robert Kett was emerging as the leader of the greatest single rising in 1549, which began at Wymondham.

In a short time the nobility and gentry restored order in the south and midlands, while troops en route for Scotland crushed rioters in Buckinghamshire, Oxfordshire and Suffolk. The Western Rebellion, based in Devon and Cornwall, largely a revolt against the new Protestant Prayer Book introduced in 1549, was a tougher nut to crack, but it was finally crushed in mid-August with heavy casualties.

In Norfolk, rioting which had begun at Attleborough in June was renewed with vigour at Wymondham after the great Fair on the weekend of 6-7 July. Here the discontented found a leader in the unlikely figure of Robert Kett who would transform an unruly mob into a purposeful demonstration against the Norfolk gentry and officials.

WYMONDHAM AND THE KETTS

Wymondham in 1549

An ancient town dominated by its Abbey, Wymondham had some 1500 people at this time. Most of the houses were clustered around the market square and adjacent streets (see map). Situated on the great highway between Norwich and London, it was a market centre of some importance in Norfolk being larger than Swaffham, Fakenham, Thetford and Attleborough. Only Norwich, Yarmouth and King's Lynn were bigger. The main ocupation of its inhabitants was agriculture, but there was a diversity of trades in the town, such as cloth, leather and wood turning, and an active guild community.

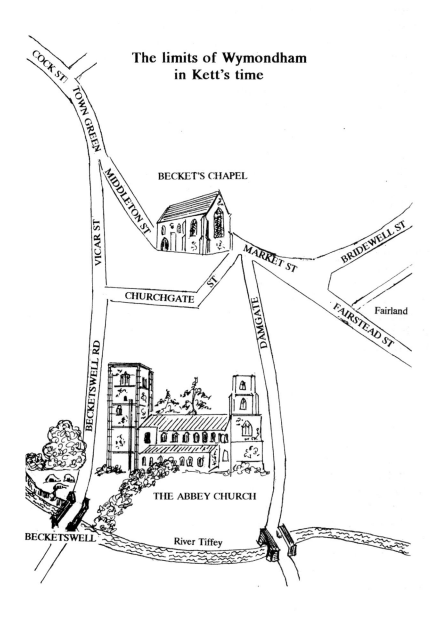

The limits of Wymondham
in Kett's time

COCK ST

TOWN GREEN

MIDDLETON ST

VICAR ST

BECKET'S CHAPEL

MARKET ST

BRIDEWELL ST

CHURCHGATE ST

FAIRSTEAD ST

Fairland

BECKETSWELL RD

DAMGATE

THE ABBEY CHURCH

BECKETSWELL

River Tiffey

The Abbey is destroyed - enter Flowerdew

In 1536 the Abbey, part of Wymondham's history since 1107 AD, was closed by Henry VIII. In charge of the dismantling of the building was a rising young lawyer the Crown Agent, John Flowerdew of Hethersett. He proceeded with great haste to despoil parts of the building and much to the parishioners annoyance, pulled down the south aisle with its dormitory above, thus exposing the nave of the parish church to all weathers. Robert and William Kett along with other leading townspeople, campaigned in 1540 to buy part of the monastery building for the town. As a result, Henry VIII granted to them the steeple and bells (lantern tower), vestry, choir, Lady Chapel, St Margaret's Chapel and the

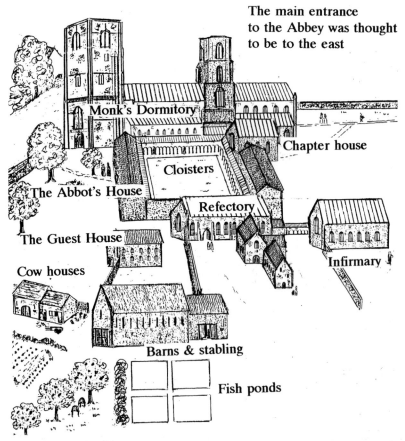

The main entrance to the Abbey was thought to be to the east

Monk's Dormitory

Chapter house

Cloisters

The Abbot's House

Refectory

The Guest House

Infirmary

Cow houses

Barns & stabling

Fish ponds

Wymondham Abbey before the Dissolution

16

remains of the south aisle (essential if the parish church was to be complete), together with Becket's Chapel in the town. The King also granted to the town, the timber of the Chapter house roof, as well as such stone and glass as would be needed for rebuilding the south aisle. However, Flowerdew seized the opportunity for his own advantage, by misappropriating lead from the roof of the monastery building, for which the parishioners had paid, together with stone from the choir, south transept and founder's wall. Such high-handedness by the Hethersett lawyer, intensified the existing bad feeling between Kett and Flowerdew, whose families were old rivals.

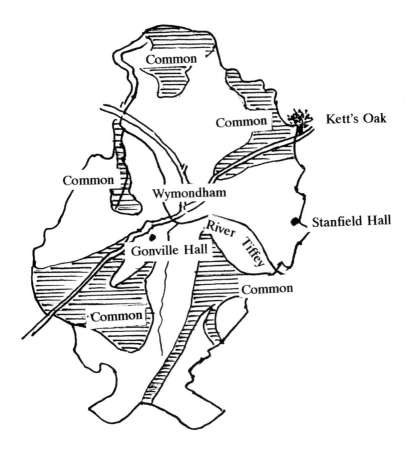

The parish of Wymondham showing the approximate areas of the commons in 1797 before they were all enclosed in 1806

Becket's Chapel

Becket's Chapel was founded in 1174 in honour of the murdered Archbishop Thomas à Becket. It was held in special affection by the townspeople, and this is why Kett and others had campaigned to retain it for the town. In 1549 the Wymondham Fair which triggered the series of events which led to Kett's Rebellion, was a festival in honour of Becket, still a popular saint in Wymondham and it is likely that mystery plays were performed inside the building which had been saved for Wymondham from the depredations of Flowerdew.

Becket's Chapel

The Ketts - 'an ancient and flourishing family'

The Kett family was an ancient one of Danish origin, which can be traced back to the 12th century. Its vitality and vigour, love of adventure, spiritual insight and openness to new ideas so characteristic of the Norsemen, were qualities clearly evident in various members of the family. The Ketts of early Norman times were bondmen, but were quick to throw off this bondage and recover their status of wealth and freedom, for they had sprung from wealthy landowning stock.

18

In Wymondham the Ketts were much influenced by the monks who educated them and they were tenants of the Abbot. They joined the guilds in the town and were very active in the Fair and mystery plays. Robert Kett's great grandfather, Richard Kett (1395-1476), was an alderman of the town and held land at Wattlefield, Suton, Norton and Silfield as well as near Becket's Chapel and in Damgate. He was a founder member of one guild, the Nativity of the Blessed Virgin (1415).

John Kett (1428-1512), the brother of Robert's grandfather, is described by Blomefield as, 'the principal landowner in Wymondham'; he was also a 'bocher' (butcher). A respected figure in the town and a member of the guilds of St Peter and St Thomas, he had been elected reeve in 1481. He was a generous benefactor and in his will bequeathed legacies to the High Altar and for church repairs, to the guild of St Thomas, various religious houses and to his relatives.

Robert Kett's father Thomas (1460-1536), farmed 20 acres in Browick and sold land in Forncett which he had inherited from his father. In Wymondham he had property in Middleton and near the Abbey. He too was a butcher and a member of the guild of the Brotherhood of Our Lady's Light.

So the immediate ancestors of Robert Kett were products of an unbroken line since about 1200, respected and respectable, a family which had steadily prospered, growing in influence and importance in Wymondham. Robert and his brother William, were to continue that tradition between 1515 and 1549.

William Kett - a man of 'desperate hardiness'
William was the eldest son of Thomas and Margery Kett. He was a butcher and mercer by trade but was, 'of more wealth than the generality of those of his business', because of his considerable properties in the Wymondham area. At various times he had land at Browick, Silfield, Norton and Northfield. In 1539 he bought Chossells Manor and in 1545, Westwode Chapel, both from John Dudley son of the Earl of Warwick, to whom William did liege service. In addition William had two shops in Churchgate Street, a tenement in Town Green and some property in Damgate. Like many of the family he was active in the life of the Wymondham guilds, being a member of the guild of Our Lady's Light and of St Thomas. He had close connections with the Abbey, leasing and later buying some of its land and acting as a server in the Abbey

Church, where he had responsibility for certain altar vessels and candles. In addition William provided timber and pitch for various repairs to the Abbey. The man who was to become Robert's loyal lieutenant during the rebellion, was therefore a good friend of the Abbey and church and a pillar of the local community. His stature must have been a great asset to Robert during the dramatic summer of 1549.

Robert Kett - 'a man of some substance'

Robert was the fourth son of Thomas and Margery and seven years younger than William. Born in 1492 he married Alice Appleyard of Braconash in 1519. They had five sons. He was a yeoman farmer and substantial landowner in the area; he also managed a tannery, probably situated by the river Tiffey near the Abbey, in the Cavick area of Wymondham where he owned two tenements.

Wymondham Abbey from Cavick

Leather was a growing industry at this time and the fact that Kett was a tanner demonstrates his enterprise and foresight. He also had property north of Becket's Chapel in Middleton and Town Green, together with a house 'in the shadow of the Abbey', possibly near his tanpits.

In the 1530s and 1540s when much land was changing hands, Robert was involved in many transactions involving nearly 100 acres. He leased land from the Abbey for a time, but in 1540 and 1547 after the Dissolution, he took the opportunity, like many others, to purchase ex-Abbey land that came on the market. In addition he rented or owned more land in Wymondham and the surrounding area (see diagram).

In 1549 his property consisted of the Manor of Wymondham, some lands belonging to the Hospital of Burton Lazars in Leicestershire, two tenements in Cavick near the 'marlepitts', including some pasture and arable land and finally, Gunvile

Manor. Here was a man with a secure and respected position in the Wymondham community, who had every reason to further consolidate his economic status.

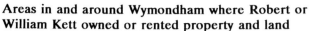

Areas in and around Wymondham where Robert or William Kett owned or rented property and land

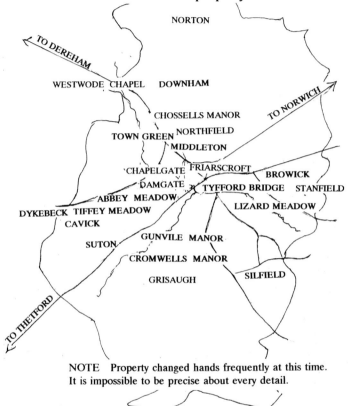

NOTE   Property changed hands frequently at this time. It is impossible to be precise about every detail.

Kett's links with the Abbey and the Guilds

Like his ancestors, Robert Kett was closely connected with the Abbey. He was educated by the monks and became a good friend of the last Abbot, naming one of his sons Loye after him.

In time he became a tenant of the Abbot and a server in the Abbey Church with responsibility for certain altar vessels and candles. After the Dissolution he campaigned to retain much of the fabric of the building for the Abbey Church, bringing him into conflict with John Flowerdew.

Kett's involvement in the local guild community is very important. The guilds were medieval in origin and primarily religious foundations. However, they did have a practical and useful role in the town, providing the members with invaluable experience in organisation and self-help. Their corporate life and sense of brotherhood were a source of strength, reinforced by annual feasts. Guild members fulfilled religious duties at the church, helped each other and gave alms to the poor. Their officers were elected and membership was largely composed of the common and middling ranks of society, women as well as men.

Robert was a member of the guilds of St Thomas and St George. He was also involved with the Watch and Play Society, a special group which provided the people of Wymondham with an outlet for their love of plays and acting. It is significant that the Lady Chapel, which had its own guild, was one of those parts of the former monastery saved for the town by the efforts of the Ketts.

The man who was to preside for six weeks over a remarkably orderly camp on Mousehold, whose principles were 'justice' and 'good governance', must have learnt many of the skills needed for its efficient administration, during his time in the Wymondham guilds. It is reasonable to suggest that the unity and co-operative spirit of the camp with its daily religious services, reflected the lessons Kett had learnt in the guilds

THE WYMONDHAM FAIR 1549

On 6 July 1549 a large crowd gathered in Wymondham for the annual fair to celebrate Thomas à Becket's appointment as Archbishop of Canterbury. There were two days of festivities and pageantry in the town including mystery plays, possibly performed in Becket's Chapel, processions and street entertainment, and doubtless much food and drink.

It was an opportunity for people to meet, talk and air their grievances, perhaps more confidently than usual because of the influence of ale. The poor of the day had good reason to be discontented as we have seen, and many would have known about the riots against enclosure in Attleborough some weeks before. Soon men were expressing their anger about certain landlords in the area who had been enclosing common land.

Action against enclosure in Morley

One of these was John Hobart, lord of the nearby manor of Morley, who had enclosed part of the common land in the village. On Monday 8 July, a group of peasants went to Morley, and pulled down Hobart's fences.

Morley Manor

Next target - Flowerdew's enclosures

Excited by their own action at Morley, the group probably joined by others went to Hethersett, where Flowerdew 'a gentleman of good estate but never expressing a desire for quiet', had enclosed part of the extensive Wymondham Common. As a lawyer and an encloser he was a special target and those with long memories would have recalled his greed at the time of the Dissolution of Wymondham Abbey (1536 -39). However, Flowerdew seems to have anticipated the trouble and succeeded, through a bribe of 40 pence, in diverting the attention of the mob to his old rival Robert Kett, who had been enclosing part of a Wymondham common, possibly the Fairland.

Flowerdew's bribe backfires

Kett's enclosing activities underline the fact that the practice was not exclusive to the big landowners of the day. Like other enterprising members of his class, he had taken the opportunities arising from a fluid land market at the time, to acquire more land for himself. The difference was that Kett came to recognise that what he was doing was unjust. On that fateful day when the mob bribed by Flowerdew arrived back in Wymondham and began to pull down Kett's fences, to the surprise of the rioters, he joined in and helped them! According to one chronicler, Kett said, 'Whatever lands I have enclosed shall be made common unto ye

23

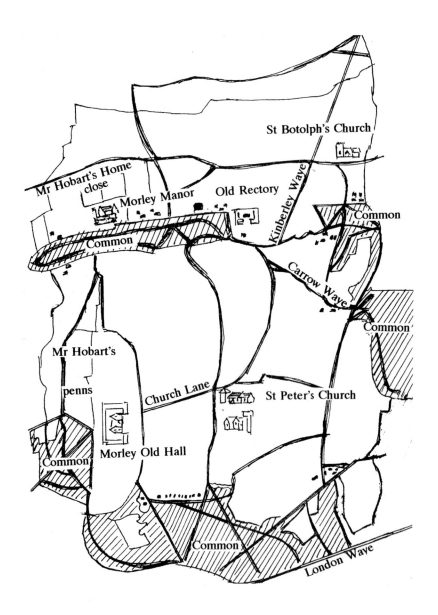

Sketch map of the parish of Morley in the early 17th century, showing the extent of the common land

and all men, and my own hand shall first perform it'. With their work complete, the group accompanied by Kett returned to Hethersett where, according to Holinshed, 'many sharp words' passed between the two men, before Flowerdew's fences were demolished. Kett would surely have enjoyed the outcome. However, the events of that day were to prove a turning point in the story, for before it was over, Kett had decided to champion the cause of the victims of enclosure.

The Kett - Flowerdew rivalry

The clash between Kett and Flowerdew on 8 July re-awakened an old feud between the two families. At the time of the Dissolution the two men clashed because Kett was closely associated with the abbey church which was looted by the ruthless and secular minded Flowerdew. A scribbled note survives from the Wymondham Churchwarden's accounts (1539) suggesting an uneasy relationship between the two families. Flowerdew was in debt to William Kett and had agreed to conditions set out by Robert Kett and others before taking up the title to land formerly in the Kett family. The rivalry between an ambitious young lawyer aspiring to the squirearchy and a down-to-earth yeoman (they had competed for land in the Stanfield and Browick areas), gave an extra dimension to the economic and social tensions in Wymondham that summer. However, Kett was concerned with much more than a personal vendetta against Flowerdew, for within a 24 hour period, presumably after much thought, he decided to associate himself with the cause of the Tudor underdog by joining the common people in their struggle against injustice.

Kett makes a surprising offer

Sometime during the evening following the drama at Hethersett and Wymondham, Kett spoke to the rioters and offered to lead them in a protest 'in defence of their common liberty'. It was a crucial point in the story, for the 'poore commons' had found a leader of such stature that the fury of an angry mob would be transformed into a purposeful demonstration, and a local squabble would be elevated into a just cause by a man whose name became inseparable from it.

Why did a relatively wealthy landowner, encloser, successful tanner and respectable pillar of the local community, offer to champion a cause which directly threatened his own interests?

Kett's motives

This subject has been a matter of continual speculation. At a time in life when Kett could have quietly tended his lands and advanced into a settled and prosperous old age, he chose instead to disregard his personal interests and become involved in a higher cause. Was this because of his religious convictions? Perhaps a deep moral sense nurtured during his education by the monks and in the life of the guilds, became outraged by the callous disregard for the plight of the poor by the great landowners. Certainly he seems to have acted after considered thought rather than on impulse during the heady atmosphere of a summer's day, or because of personal animosity towards Flowerdew.

At any rate his intervention provided the 'poore commons' with an outstanding leader. It seems that on the evening of 8 July and perhaps next morning, Kett spoke to his followers with words which clearly reveal his aims and underline his personal commitment to the cause. He wanted to 'subdue the power of great men' and make them regret their 'pride'. Further, he indicated his willingness to put his life on the line by saying he was ready 'to sacrifice my substance', and 'my very life itself', because, 'so highly do I esteem the cause in which we are engaged'. Kett was clearly the kind of man who would stand up for what he believed was right. He had already done so in the campaign against Flowerdew's despoliation of the Wymondham Abbey Church. Now he did so again over an issue which seemed to him clear-cut.

THE MARCH TO NORWICH

On 9 July Kett and his followers assembled at an oak tree outside Wymondham. At this stage the plan seems to have been to march to Norwich, England's second city, and establish a camp as a demonstration against local injustice, hopefully persuading the gentry to mend their ways. At the same time many hoped for the support of the 'good duke' Protector Somerset in London, as he was believed to be sympathetic to the poor. The spirits of the Norfolk poor on that march were much raised by the leader that events had brought to the centre of their affairs. However, though it can be said that the situation of 1549 had produced the man, it would be the man who made the cause.

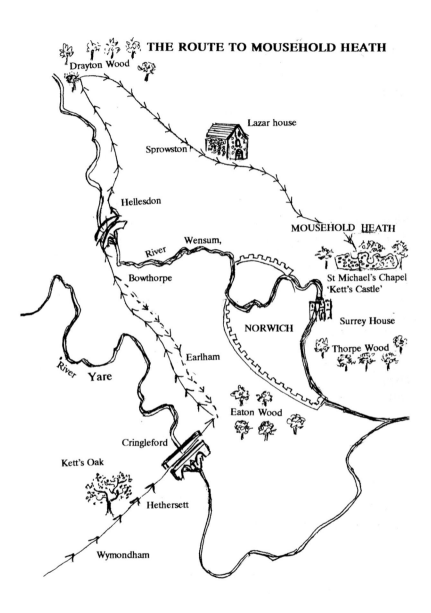

THE ROUTE TO MOUSEHOLD HEATH

Drayton Wood

Lazar house

Sprowston

Hellesdon

MOUSEHOLD HEATH

River Wensum,

St Michael's Chapel
'Kett's Castle'

Bowthorpe

NORWICH

Surrey House

Earlham

Thorpe Wood

River Yare

Eaton Wood

Cringleford

Kett's Oak

Hethersett

Wymondham

The story of the march to Norwich 9 - 12 July

9 July The marchers left 'Kett's Oak' outside Wymondham crossing the river Yare at Cringleford. Then they went via Eaton and Earlham to Bowthorpe, where they made a camp. News of the marchers soon reached Norwich, where messengers were sent to London and appeals for help were made to Sir Roger Townshend at Raynham and Sir William Paston at Caister. At this point it seems that a mob from Norwich pulled down the fences of the Town Close and then joined Kett at Bowthorpe. Two attempts were made to disperse the Bowthorpe camp firstly by Sir Edmund Windham, Sheriff of Norfolk who declared those assembled there to be rebels and ordered them to go home, and secondly by the Mayor of Norwich Thomas Codd, who seems to have used more moderate language. However, neither were successful.

10 July Doubtless aware that the city authorities had appealed to London, the marchers returned to Eaton Wood and tried to get permission to pass through Norwich as a direct route to Mousehold Heath, a good site for a more permanent camp. However, the city councillors alarmed by events refused access to the marchers. It is possibly at the second camp at Eaton that the 'Rebels Complaint' was drawn up, an early statement of rebel aspirations:

> *'We will leave no stone unturned to obtain our rights, nor will we give over until things are settled as we wish them to be. What we want is liberty, and the power, in common with our so-called superiors, of enjoying the gifts of nature'.*

Remains of St. Michael's Chapel – 'Kett's Castle'

11 July Thwarted by the city authorities they turned north and crossed the river Wensum at Hellesdon. Near here they were confronted by Sir Roger Wodehouse of Kimberley, who offered them bribes of food and drink as an inducement to return home. However, Wodehouse was captured, his provisions commandeered and he was the first gentleman to become a prisoner of the demonstrators. That evening Kett made a temporary camp at Drayton Woods.

12 July Next day Kett's force steadily growing in strength, moved round the north of the city through Sprowston towards Mousehold. En route they destroyed the dovecote of John Corbet, a lawyer-cum-landowner. This was located in St Mary Magdalen Chapel, part of the Lazar House or hospital founded in 1196 (now a library). Like hedges around common land which the marchers pulled down, dovecotes were disliked by the poor because the pigeons destroyed the crops of the small arable farmers. On reaching Mousehold Heath they occupied Surrey House the former residence of the Earl of Surrey, executed in Henry VIII's reign. The building was used in part to imprison some of the rebel captives. At this stage these included Wodehouse and a few lawyers including Sergeants Gawdy and Gatlyn and the Appleyard brothers of Stanfield, close allies of Flowerdew. Kett also took over the deserted St Michael's Chapel, making it the headquarters of his camp. It soon became known as 'Kett's Castle', and its superb view over Norwich would give the rebels a distinct strategic advantage in the military struggle that lay ahead.

KETT'S CAMP SEEKS A 'BETTER DAY'

Kett and his followers stayed on Mousehold Heath for nearly seven weeks. Until 21 July there was an uneasy peace with Norwich when rebels and townspeople mixed without violence. Thereafter Norwich was officially hostile territory, though a fifth column of sympathizers in the city joined the camp during this phase. The period from 22 July to 26 August was dominated by tactical and military considerations such as keeping the city in order, trying to spread the rebellion to other towns and preparing to meet the royal armies which were sent against them.

Other camps swell Mousehold's numbers

Although Kett's Camp on Mousehold was the centre-piece of the Norfolk Rising, several other camps were formed in Norfolk during the unrest. Perhaps the most important was at Castle Rising where men gathered from King's Lynn, Downham and the villages of West Norfolk. The Ryston Oak seems to have been a rallying point for the discontented in the area. Nearby they sacked Ryston Farm, leaving this note for the landowner:

'Mr Pratt, your sheep are very fat, and we thank you for that,
We have left you the skins to pay your lady's pins,
And you must thank us for that'.

The local gentry dispersed the rebels who failed to take King's Lynn and then moved via Brandon and Thetford to Watton, before finally marching to Mousehold. Meanwhile at Hingham another rebel camp tried to seize Sir Edmund Knyvett's stronghold of Old Buckenham Castle, but failed; they too marched to join Kett at Norwich. Across the border in Suffolk, rebels in the Bungay and Beccles area tried unsuccessfully to capture Yarmouth, before joining Kett. By 20 July Kett's Camp was probably 10,000 strong.

A Camp but also a seat of government

Although the camp at Mousehold was a base for a great protest demonstration against injustice, it was also much more. Mousehold was the seat of government of Kett's new state. There was a court to administer justice and a council with advisers who decided on policies and issued warrants and commissions, and which drew up the 29 Requests or reforms sent to the King. Kett's Camp saw the creation of a rudimentary system of democratic representation. Each of the 24 hundreds represented at the camp elected two councillors or 'Governors'. The map shows that two thirds of Norfolk were involved, some 15,000 people or more, from many villages and towns in the county.

The 24 Hundreds represented at Kett's Camp

To administer the camp Kett had a kind of secretariat composed of a few scholars and clergymen who acted as scribes, drafting and writing documents issued by Kett, which observed due form and procedure. This attention to administrative detail reflected the orderliness of Kett's camp. One of the key figures in this was Thomas Godsalve, son of the Controller of the Mint Sir John

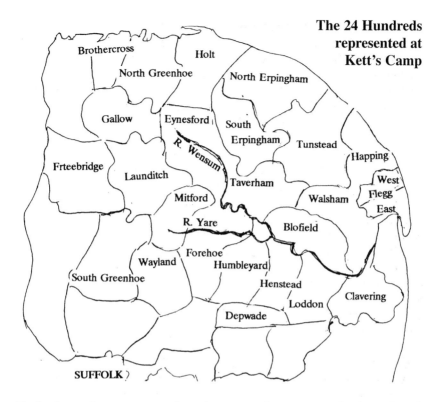

The 24 Hundreds represented at Kett's Camp

Brothercross

Holt

North Greenhoe

North Erpingham

Gallow

Eynesford

South Erpingham

Tunstead

Happing

R. Wensum

Frteebridge

Launditch

Taverham

West Flegg

Mitford

Walsham

East

R. Yare

Blofield

Forehoe

Wayland

Humbleyard

South Greenhoe

Henstead

Clavering

Loddon

Depwade

SUFFOLK

Godsalve, who was an early prisoner at the camp and whose legal expertise, education and administrative skill would have been invaluable. In effect he became Kett's secretary of state.

Kett also enlisted key figures from Norwich's political elite in discussions at the camp, including the mayor Thomas Codd, and the senior and much respected alderman Thomas Aldrich, together with Robert Watson a popular and influential 'new' preacher. He persuaded Kett to appoint Tom Coniers a clergyman at St Martin's Church to be chaplain to the camp. Daily religious services using Cranmer's new Protestant Prayer Book became another feature of life on Mousehold.

Kett's aim was to establish a machinery of government to replace the broken-down county administration. It was open, democratic and devoid of tyranny or rough justice. The 'Governors' were, like Kett, men of some standing in their own communities such as, reeves, small farmers, craftsmen and shopkeepers – an alternative 'County Council'.

Many of the early accounts of the rebellion were hostile to Kett, stressing the violence and disorder of the camp. However, there is little evidence to support this and only a camp with a proper adminstration and code of behaviour could have kept such a vast crowd in good discipline for so long. Visitors to the camp such as Codd, Aldrich, Watson and Matthew Parker, a future archbishop of Canterbury, were received with courtesy, given a dignified hearing and granted free expression of their opinions. When the first Royal Herald arrived on 21 July he was similarly treated.

Organising the food supply

The first challenge for Kett was to ensure that his 10-15,000 followers were fed. Exposed on a bleak hill, the camp would surely have collapsed with countless desertions had not the administration provided regular food and provisions. In fact for six weeks, Mousehold became a real community and home for thousands who built turf huts and rough shacks with the timber from Thorpe Wood. There were of course plentiful supplies of food in the rich estates around Norwich and further afield. Raiding parties were authorised to scour the countryside and commandeer cattle, sheep, corn, geese, chicken, deer etc. Kett seems to have made every effort to control these activities and prevent abuse or unbridled looting. During this process there was no injury to person or property, a further illustration of his moderation. Tom Wodehouse of Waxham complained that he had been despoiled of, 'all my bullocks and horses and most of my corn', but the claim by one chronicler that '20,000 sheep, 4,000 oxen and thousands of poultry were consumed in a few days' is clearly an exaggeration. Furthermore, Kett issued Warrants in the King's name, couched in proper legal form to avoid antagonising the populace and to convey constitutional propriety.

> *'We, the Kings friends and deputies, do grant license to all men to provide and bring into the camp at Mousehold,all manner of cattle and provisions of victuals, in what places soever they may find the same, so that no violence or injury be done to any honest or pooreman, commanding all persons as they tender the King's honour and royal majesty and the relief of the commonwealth, to be obedient to us the Governors and to those whose names ensue'.*

Signatures of Kett, Codd and Aldrich

The Warrants were signed by Kett, but also Codd and Aldrich the civic leaders of Norwich, who were persuaded to co-operate in Kett's great social experiment.

Managing the food supply for the camp was thus achieved by a considerable degree of central policy and control. By such means were provisions brought to Mousehold, and many must have enjoyed their first regular food for some time.

That this was at the expense of local farmers is revealed in a letter from a farmer's wife addressed to the Camp Secretariat. Although she had freely supplied some sheep to the Mousehold camp as a gesture of support, a further 189 of her best animals had been taken away by rebels. Her letter was a polite request for compensation, evidence perhaps of orderly arrangements at the camp to deal with such claims, even though Kett and his fellow Governors had large numbers to feed and faced mounting political and military pressures. The letter provides a fascinating glimpse into the relationship between a farmer and Kett's camp.

The Oak of Reformation

When the provisions arrived at the camp their orderly distribution took place in public to ensure fairness, almost certainly beneath the spreading boughs of a great oak. This tree became the symbol of the order and idealism of Kett's camp. The famous court of justice held at the Oak of Reformation probably originated in the arrangements for receiving these provisions and stores. Here disputes between Kett's men about the provisions were settled, and 'the covetous and greedy', were charged with appropriating supplies meant for the common good. Here too complaints were heard about oppressive landlords or lawyers who became prisoners on Mousehold, if found guilty. It was a short step from being a delivery and distribution point for food and supplies, to that of a court of justice. At the the Oak of Reformation trials were open and fair and the prisoners suffered no violence or injury. Finally, it is worth noting that daily religious services were conducted from here, and Mathew Parker preached a sermon urging the rebels to disperse.

Wale delin.

Page Sculp.

Taken from Ashburton's History of England, 1793

A start is made in tackling grievances

Once on Mousehold Kett needed to convince the camp that the protest would bring about change. Many of his followers had travelled long distances, and taking part in what would be a long demonstration they would be sacrificing family life, losing income and crops, not to say endangering their own lives by joining the camp. They needed assurance that it was all worthwhile, that better conditions would come about and the gentry would be brought to heel.

One of the first ways Kett showed he meant reform and was determined to redress grievances was to put on trial those gentry and lawyers who had been captured in the first days of the Rising. The trials were held under the Oak of Reformation and there was doubtless some rowdiness by the rougher elements in the camp, who according to Sotherton's account which is hostile to Kett, shouted 'Hang him', 'Kill him', during the trials. However, Kett's judicial procedures prevented any rough justice or mob violence by such groups. It is yet another example of his moderation and strict observance of legal form. Only two cases are recorded of harassment of prisoners, but neither was injured and there were certainly no public hangings. Those found guilty of maladminstration were imprisoned in Surrey House. Kett's camp was a reformed state not a tyranny.

Reform - the Twenty Nine Requests

The Rebels Complaint issued at Eaton Woods whilst on the march to Norwich, had indicated the general aspirations of the rebels, including the phrase, 'we desire liberty and a fair use of all things'. Now Kett and his fellow Governors drew up a list of their main grievances which would be sent as a petition to the King. It was soon apparent that the rebels had many concerns apart from enclosure which had been uppermost in their minds until they arrived at Mousehold.

The document known as the 'Twenty Nine Requests' is a random list not a coherent programme of reform, produced in some haste by Kett and others during the first week of the camp. However it does indicate the main grievances of the rebels. Above all they are concerned with the fair administration of the laws governing property, common rights to land and reasonable rents. They are also concerned with prices and abuses of the law by local officials and gentry, which caused economic hardship to the lower orders.

The rebel leaders were decent, honest, industrious men appealing for fair treatment which they were not getting in Norfolk, because the judicial and administrative processes were controlled by the local gentry and lawyers rather than the Crown. In particular they wanted to curb the powers of the Escheator and Feodary as both could make excessive legal demands on small famers. Perhaps some would have cause to remember that Flowerdew was the Escheator in 1548.

In many respects it is a conservative document trying to recapture an imaginary 'golden age' in the reign of Henry VII (1485-1509), when landlords paid their own rents and dues instead of passing them off on their tenants, kept their beasts off the common, made fishing and hunting rights freely available, and controlled dovecotes and rabbit coneys - in short fulfilled their obligations as landowners responsibly. The rebels did not wish to overthrow a propertied society, but to re-establish it on a basis of social and economic justice. The petition is essentially moderate in tone and scrupulously respectful of the King's authority. Kett's slogans were 'justice' and 'good governance' and the reforms aimed at restraining unrestricted rural capitalism and curbing gentry power in the courts and the countryside. There was no threat of mob rule.

The rebels also wanted church ministers to perform their pastoral duties competently, through preaching, teaching poor children, staying resident in their parish and having no office outside the church.

Finally, the rebels appealed to the King to sanction the popular 'alternative' government set up on Mousehold to 'redress and reform' all the laws and proclamations which had been 'hidden' by his corrupt officials in Norfolk from the 'poore commons' since Henry VII's reign. It was a remarkable request to a beleaguered government from a community which had shown itself capable of managing its affairs in difficult conditions, with considerable skill. There was no threat to the King.

The rebel leaders were men with some stake in society - small farmers, self-employed craftsmen and shopkeepers in conflict with the large farmers and lawyers. Although the poorest in Norfolk are not represented in the petition, they still looked to Kett as their champion. The most famous of the 29 Requests stating,

'We pray that all bond men may be made free, for God made all free with his precious blood shedding',

is an eloquent plea for society to be based on Christian principles of egalitarianism by the removal of the institution of villeinage, a medieval hangover. Kett may have been a leader with a respected and comfortable background, but this did not preclude his concern for the underdog in Tudor Norfolk.

The importance of Kett's Camp on Mousehold
Kett's camp was the orderly symbol of a great demonstration by men united by a sense of purpose and good fellowship, with God and the Commonweal (common good) in their minds. For nearly seven weeks morale remained high and despite exhausting military engagements against mounting odds, there was no significant loss of discipline until the very end, a great tribute to Kett's leadership.

The camp was a noble and unique venture yet its expectations were both improbable and naive. But in mid 16th century England there was no other way for the lower orders to make their views heard against injustice. So united by its hatred of the gentry and inspired by a great leader, the camp represented Norfolk's sturdy spirit of self-reliance in its determined struggle to achieve social and economic justice.

The first week of the camp 13-20 July
Though Norwich was initially hostile to Kett and had refused to let him through the city to Mousehold, once there, Kett seems to have established a working relationship with the civic authorities. He persuaded Mayor Codd and Thomas Aldrich, a much respected alderman to work with him on Mousehold. Mindful of the existence of a fifth column of sympathizers in Norwich for Kett, the city government wisely agreed to allow the camp free access for food, funds and supplies which supplemented what was being brought in from the surrounding estates. So began an uneasy peace between Norwich and Mousehold, as both sides waited for a response from London, Norwich hoping for help to evict its unwelcome new neighbours and Kett for a favourable reply to the 29 Requests.

On 13 July a royal commission ordered Robert Watson, a popular and influential 'new preacher', to persuade the camp to disperse. He failed but Kett accepted his recommendation that Thomas Coniers of St Martin's Church, become chaplain. Thereafter daily Protestant services were held at the camp.

On the same day Mathew Parker a Cambridge scholar and a rising star in the Anglican Church preached at the Oak of Reformation. He appealed for moderation and patience, warned against bloodshed and urged the leaders to abandon their enterprise. Though he was heard with courtesy at first, the feeling grew that he was the lackey of the landlords and while Coniers distracted the crowd with the 'Te Deum', Parker made his retreat. Next day Parker preached in St Clement's Church in Norwich against the rebellion antagonising some rebels in the congregation. Having made himself unpopular, he wisely left Norwich the following day.

On 15 July Leonard Sotherton a wealthy merchant set off for London to seek help for Norwich. Meanwhile, Kett was consolidating his position and setting up the machinery of government which would administer the camp. More landlords and lawyers were taken prisoner and held as bargaining counters for the reforms he was seeking. The first trials were held under the Oak of Reformation, but there was no maltreatment of the prisoners, and the precedent was set for moderate and humane conduct. Warrants were issued to obtain essential victuals as well as guns and powder, the latter a sensible precaution against anticipated retaliation by a vengeful gentry. Finally, the 29 Requests were drawn up by the rebel leaders representing the 24 Hundreds, and sent to the King. So while the city was asking the King for help in dispersing the camp, Kett was appealing to the King for help in reforming Norfolk. During this week despite the fears of some of the citizens, Norwich was neither looted nor subject to a reign of terror by lawless mobs.

The Courtyard of Stranger's Hall – the home of the Sotherton family

FIRST PARDON AND FIRST BLOOD

The arrival of the Royal Herald on 21 July brought the uneasy peace to an end, concluding a particular phase in the story of the Norfolk Rising. Until now tensions in Norfolk between landlord and tenant or the governing class and the governed had dominated the scene. Now, local politics merged into national affairs; a demonstration became rebellion and military conflict inevitable.

A Pardon is offered and rejected

The King's Council was busy with rebellion in the West Country and the Midlands and so an official pardon was to be offered to Kett's men provided they dispersed. Along with a pardon was the King's reply to the 29 Requests which offered little and promised less, warning that it would be unwise if he was 'driven by necessity' to adopt 'sharper means' to maintain his own dignity.

Protector Somerset hoped that the offer of a pardon would solve the problem on Mousehold. The Herald went to the camp and was greeted with cheers and 'God save the King' by some who were perhaps ready to accept the royal mercy. However, Kett was convinced he was no traitor and believing the law and certainly justice, were on his side, he rejected the pardon giving this trenchant repy to the Herald:

> *'Kings and princes are want to pardon wicked persons not innocent and just men. We...have deserved nothing and are guilty ourselves of no crime, and therefore we despise such speeches as idle and unprofitable to our business.. I trust I have done nothing but what belongs to the duty of a true subject'.*

It was a courageous reply and he seemed to have dissuaded waverers in the camp from joining the Herald. However, the rejection of the pardon was a turning point in the story, for thereafter, Kett's followers were seen as rebels and traitors.

The Battle for Bishopgate Bridge - 22 July

Unable to arrest Kett because of the size of his force, the Herald retired to Norwich accompanied by Mayor Codd and a few others. Bishopgate Bridge, the weakest point of the city's defences facing Mousehold was closed and reinforced with earth, while guards were set on the other gates in the city. What followed was the result of royal policy, for Norwich could no longer co-operate with Kett, neither did it have the resources to resist him. At the same time Kett needed to maintain open access to the city for food and supplies.

Codd did what he could to strengthen the defences. He released the prisoners the rebels had put in the Castle and the Guildhall, and placed the city cannon and two larger guns provided by Sir William Paston from Caister Castle on the Castle banks facing Mousehold. Men were employed making shot for the gunners and one gun was placed on the common staithe to be more in range of the camp. Elsewhere, the locks on several gates were mended in a hasty effort to keep the rebels out of the city until the government sent reinforcements.

The type of cannon used during the Rebellion

In an attempt to avoid bloodshed Kett offered a truce which was rejected. Then began an artillery exchange, but neither side had the skill nor sufficient powder to cause serious damage. So the rebels made a direct attack on Bishopgate Bridge which was defended by archers, but they proved inadequate against the fury and numbers of the rebels, whose reckless courage appears to have terrified the defenders. According to Sotherton, the rebel force included vagabond boys, who though 'naked and unarmed' fearlessly defied the shower of arrows, then gathered them up even though some had 'stuck to their legs and other parts'. Then they plucked them from their bodies and gave them 'all dripping with blood' to the rebel archers who used them to fire back at the defenders. It was easy for the rebels to outflank the bridge by swimming the river, which they did in large numbers so driving off the defenders. Norwich quickly fell to the rebels.

Bishop Bridge today

The rebels control Norwich 22 - 31 July

With the route from Mousehold to the city re-opened once more, Kett's men took captured guns back to the camp together with military stores kept in the Guildhall, such as powder, shot, halberds, bills, staves, bows and arrows. These the City Chamberlain was compelled to surrender, but there was no arbitrary violence.

Later that day the Herald offered a second pardon which was dismissed as 'empty promises'. Realising his action had put Norwich in rebel hands he left for London. Kett was now master of Norwich. Most of the city's weapons were in his hands while his men guarded strategic points. The rebels also occupied churches and other public buildings. However, most could not be accommodated in this way and after the fighting, they returned to Mousehold.

All these events alarmed many of the citizens, but though some of Kett's men were not above petty theft or accepting bribes, there was no random violence or still worse, arbitrary killings. Most of the civic leaders were imprisoned in Surrey House on Mousehold. However, Kett agreed to Aldrich's suggestion that Mayor Codd should be released. Codd preferred to remain at the rebel camp and appointed his deputy Augustine Steward to administer Norwich on behalf of Kett and his fellow leaders.

The lull before the storms 24 - 31 July

Kett had entered Norwich by force and rejected a royal pardon, so he must have realised that it was only a matter of time before troops were sent against him. Yet the moderation and humanity which characterised his camp from the beginning, continued to prevail in Norwich. Though there must have been many vagabonds and lawless elements who wanted to exploit the situation, no injury was done to the citizens and the initial looting was quickly checked. At the camp, trials continued at the Oak of Reformation but the worst those found guilty could expect, was to be imprisoned in Surrey House. Some city merchants were probably outraged at the fun made of the Mayor, with jokes about a 'Cod's head for a penny', but this was merely a symptom of the good humour in the camp. In Norwich, Steward's management of daily affairs under Kett's oversight, ensured a period remarkably free of wanton plunder and destruction.

As beacons and church bells spread the news that the 'poore commons' had raised a standard, people from the quiet villages and market towns of Norfolk joined the bold spirits and swelling numbers at Kett's Camp, now probably over 15,000 strong. Under Kett's leadership the lower orders had found a champion who made an impact on the ruling class of Norfolk. Among the many small communities which sent contingents to Mousehold was North Elmham.

The North Elmham contingent at Mousehold

The surviving churchwardens' accounts for the township provide glimpses of the impact of Kett's Rebellion on a small community. Most of the men who went to Kett's Camp from North Elmham were married with families, and included one of the churchwardens Henry Ruston. The other churchwarden William Dyks organised the supply and delivery of victuals to Thomas Powle, the constable of North Elmham at the camp. Ruston claimed part of his wages and expenses from parish funds for use of his horse and cart for the frequent journeys he presumably made between North Elmham and Mousehold. The parish also paid for the repair of his harness. Other men including Henry Wakefield, Clement Crow, Richard Watson and John Wright were also paid for carrying provisions to Mousehold including, fish, bread, mustard, garlic, onions, meat, salt and beer, the latter brewed by one of the wives, Mrs Dyks

The parish authority gave its full 'assent and consent' to volunteers from the village joining the camp by providing money, supplies and organisational backing.

North Elmham Church

This support must have been a considerable drain on the resources of the parish, apart from the hardship caused to those families whose menfolk were away for several weeks. Wages of three pence a day were paid to the men at the camp, Robert Clerke receiving three shillings and four pence for 'being the cook at the camp' for one month (presumably for the North Elmham men). Apart from the wages and expenses for those who carried provisions to Mousehold, payments were also made to Mrs Fylde and Mrs Clerke whose husbands were at the camp, for food and drink, for repairing Thomas Tott's 'bowe and strings' and buying staves and arrowheads. The parish also paid for 'healing' Thomas Wakefield, who was injured in the hand and face at the first 'skyrmish'. Before the last 'skyrmish' Thomas Tott and his company were given 14 pence for 'to drynck with by the way'.

All this indicates not only active support for Kett but orderly management, for two groups were sent to Mousehold and became an integral part of the camp. It was probably not untypical of the response of many villages where men were drawn to Norwich by the magnet of the Wymondham tanner.

REBELS AGAINST ROYAL ARMIES

The Protector sends troops

After Kett had rejected the pardon, Somerset had no option but to to use military force to suppress the rebellion and he ordered the Earl of Northampton to raise an army. This force included courtiers, noblemen, a famous siege engineer Sir Richard Lee and 300 Italian mercenaries. Leading Norfolk gentry, recognising the seriousness of Kett's Rebellion also joined Northampton, including Sir Thomas Paston, Sir Henry Parker, Sir Henry Bedingfeld and Sir Thomas Cornwallis. However, though the army had a professional core and considerable military experience, it was only some 1400 strong.

Northampton's army enters Norwich

By 31 July the royal army was outside Norwich. The Herald ordered the city to surrender but only after Steward had consulted Codd who was still on Mousehold with Kett, were the gates opened. Presumably Kett judged that the rebel army was strong enough to deal with Northampton who was entering a divided city, for although many of the citizens were loyal to him, others were sympathetic to Kett. While his army made the market place its base, Northampton took council in the Guildhall. It was decided to close the gates against the rebel camp and guard the key points of the city's defences.

That evening, some Italian mercenaries strayed outside the city and became involved in a skirmish with some rebels. One of the mercenaries was captured, taken up to Mousehold and summarily hanged by Cayme of Bungay. The rebels had a special hatred for foreign troops being used to support the gentry, and one account suggests the unfortunate soldier was hanged 'for his apparel's sake'. Though Kett could not have known about this incident, it may indicate that at this point others at the rebel camp were taking the initiative.

As a result of this incident, Northampton strengthened his guards and consolidated his hold on the Castle area and Cathedral Close. He then went to Steward's house in Tombland where his party was lavishly entertained. However, such was the anxiety of Northampton's entourage that night, that they kept their armour on when they retired to bed. It was a wise decision.

A night of bloodshed - 31 July

During the night the rebels began an artillery attack but their guns did little damage. It was the prelude to a mass assault from Mousehold and as there were rebels in the city, fighting occurred in the streets as well as near the walls and gates.

The rebels climbed the city walls or swam the river, fighting fiercely and desperately. Many were killed and others suffered terrible wounds, but despite the ferocity of the attack the city's defences held. Something of the fury and drama of this night battle is captured in the vivid account of Neville which implies unwitting respect for the rebels' courage.

> *'Many were drowned in their own and other men's blood; even at the last gasp they furiously withstood our men. Yea many also stricken through their breasts with swords and the sinews of their legs cut asunder, yet creeping on their knees were moved with such fury as they wounded our soldiers, lying amongst the slain almost without life'.*

After three terrible hours over 300 rebels lay dead in the dark before the attackers finally withdrew to Mousehold. Their undaunted courage and determined spirit is remarkable.

Rebel victory on St Martin's Plain - 1 August

Next morning while the city's gates were being repaired, Northampton took breakfast in the Maid's Head. To avoid further conflict he decided to offer another pardon. Steward accompanied the Herald to Pockthorpe Gate, where a large crowd of rebels appeared. The pardon which was dependent on the rebels ceasing their 'outrages', was once again rejected, this time by one Flotman. His reply was similar in tone and content to that of Kett ten days earlier, announcing that they were loyal subjects not traitors and would continue to struggle to obtain social and economic justice from the gentlemen.

As this was happening another group of rebels attacked Bishopgate Bridge with renewed vigour; this was the weakest point in the city defences. In another bloody engagement, some swam the river while others attacked the gate which soon fell, leaving the street beyond the bridge open for the rebels to advance towards the city centre.

As they swarmed along Bishopgate, their advance was blocked by Northampton's guns and troops which were deployed on St Martin's Plain behind the Cathedral.

St. Martin's Plain

The fighting was fierce but the sheer exuberance of the rebels and their superior numbers overwhelmed the royal force, whose cannons were captured by a flank attack along lanes by the river. But the most dramatic moment came with the death of Lord Sheffield, Northampton's deputy. He was unhorsed in the mêlée and though he tried to save himself by removing his visor to show he was a peer, the rebels were in no mood for chivalry and Sheffield was despatched by Fulke the butcher.

The battle was over by noon; Northampton's forces defeated and demoralised, withdrew in disorder with 100 casualties; a further 30 became prisoners of Kett including Sir Henry Bedingfeld and Sir Thomas Cornwallis. Lord Sheffield and 35 others killed in this battle were later buried in St Martin's churchyard. It is impossible to be exact about rebel casualties though they could have been as high as 130.

Norwich in rebel hands

The rebel victory on St Martin's Plain greatly boosted morale. Kett's men had humiliated a royal army but there now followed a few days of some civil disorder, though we should be wary of accepting the hostile accounts which portray the rebels pillaging and destroying the city wantonly. They quickly overran Norwich and many of the wealthy citizens fled along with the remnants of

46

Northampton's army. Inevitably some empty houses were plundered next day but Kett had no wish to destroy a city on whose resources and trade his camp depended. There was damage to some property, particularly that of rich merchants because feeling amongst the poor of Norwich against them, was as strong as that felt by the rural community towards the gentry. But there was no orchestrated campaign to fire the city and no recorded incidents of violence towards people. Kett's restraint, moderation and humanity continued. It is worth remembering that the rebels had lost relatives and friends in the recent bloody conflicts. In the elation of victory it would be surprising if there had not been a temporary loss of discipline in a time of such turmoil.

The restraint of the rebels is illustrated at Augustine Steward's house in Tombland when they came looking for Northampton and other gentlemen. Having searched his house and found no one, they left after looting his shop. Steward was unharmed and after someone pointed out they would be hanged for looting, it soon stopped and they contented themselves with making the servants of the merchants who had fled, bake them bread. Those who feared the worst need not have done so and the suggestion that only rain saved the city from a terrible fate is grossly exaggerated. The Victoria County History is much nearer the mark with this judgment:

> 'That a populous and wealthy city.....should have been for 3 weeks in the hands of 20,000 rebels, and should have escaped utter pillage and ruin, speaks highly for the rebel leaders'

Kett restores order in Norwich

The events of the previous days, with the intense military pressures, suggest that other rebel leaders were exercising some influence on tactics. However, Kett continued in an active and directing role even though his control was less complete than in the heady weeks of July.

The presence of rebels roaming freely in the city caused some anxiety, but the looting and intimidation was shortlived. Kett's influence is seen in the return to some normality after a few days, with Steward re-instated as the civic leader.

Kett established a stronger presence by setting up a garrison camp in the cathedral grounds, posting a lookout on the spire and putting guards on the city gates. Some of the rebel's prisoners were kept in the Castle and Guildhall. But he was just as concerned

Augustine Steward's house in Tombland

to restore adminstrative order in Norwich appointing aldermen and constables from his own men who operated under Steward's overlordship. Again during these weeks there was no mistreatment of citizens or prisoners reflecting the inner morality which had marked the rebellion from the start. He even used preachers to influence his men positively.

Attempts to spread the rebellion

With a royal army defeated and Norwich now completely under rebel control, Kett must have realised that further military confrontation was inevitable unless he could negotiate a settlement. While other smaller camps at Castle Rising, Watton and Hingham had been dispersed by local gentry resulting in these rebels swelling the numbers on Mousehold, Kett recognised the need to broaden his power base.

On 5 August an attempt was made to seize Yarmouth a strategically important and prosperous port, whose capture would also have guaranteed a regular supply of fish to Mousehold. A Warrant was issued signed by Kett and Aldrich at the 'King's Camp' demanding that Yarmouth act as a garrison against Kett's enemies. However, the town refused to co-operate and admit the 100 men Kett sent, sending messengers to London asking for help instead. Another attempt to capture the port took place on 17 August when Kett sent a larger force with six cannon from Lowestoft. They were again repulsed and the defenders, firing a haystack and counter-attacking under cover of smoke, captured 30 rebels. One more unsuccessful attempt was made to break into Yarmouth before the rebels returned to Mousehold. As at King's Lynn, the rebels were thwarted at Yarmouth by the combined efforts of the local gentry and townsmen.

A second royal army is prepared - 18 August

Meanwhile Protector Somerset was preparing to lead a much bigger army to suppress Kett, but once the rebellion in Devon had been dealt with he decided to put the Earl of Warwick in charge of this force, which was ready to march by 18 August. Initially there were 7,500 men, including 2,000 cavalry, 3,000 infantry, artillery and mercenaries from Italy and the Netherlands. This army was reinforced by more soldiers as well as local gentry as it marched to Norfolk.

A royal proclamation had ordered the gentry of Essex and Suffolk to be ready while those in Norfolk would join Warwick as he approached Norwich. Warwick's force was much more formidable than the one led by Northampton which had been overwhelmed by Kett, being composed of battle-hardened professionals who had served in France or Scotland. Among these was the redoubtable Captain Drury who commanded a squadron of some 200 arquebusiers who served with distinction. Warwick himself was an experienced and able commander and second only to Protector Somerset in power and influence; furthermore he was very ambitious.

St. Stephen's Gate

WARWICK'S MARCH TO NORWICH

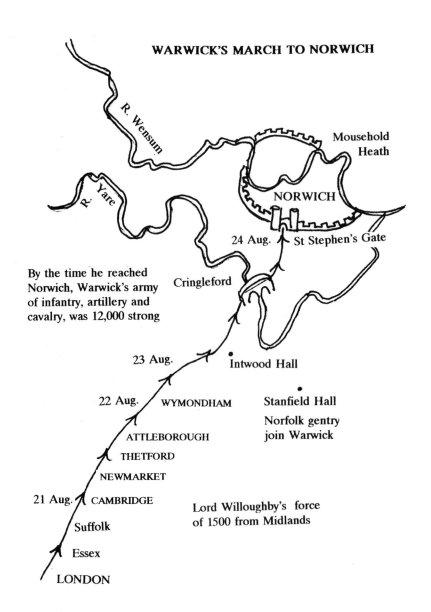

R. Wensum

Mousehold Heath

R. Yare

NORWICH

24 Aug. St Stephen's Gate

By the time he reached Norwich, Warwick's army of infantry, artillery and cavalry, was 12,000 strong

Cringleford

23 Aug.   Intwood Hall

22 Aug.   WYMONDHAM   Stanfield Hall

ATTLEBOROUGH   Norfolk gentry join Warwick

THETFORD

NEWMARKET

21 Aug. CAMBRIDGE   Lord Willoughby's force of 1500 from Midlands

Suffolk

Essex

LONDON

50

Warwick's army reached the outskirts of Norwich on 24 August by which time it numbered some 12,000 men. Even so, he wanted to avoid battle if possible given the strength of Kett's position on Mousehold and he knew that holding Norwich once he had entered it would be very difficult.

Warwick's Herald offers a pardon - 24 August

When the Herald approached St Stephen's Gate to order Norwich to admit Warwick's army, Kett sent out a deputation comprising Steward and an alderman to negotiate. They suggested a pardon be offered which was duly agreed by Warwick. Perhaps Kett now realised, because he was perceived as a rebel, that to fight another battle would do nothing to advance the rebel cause. To accept the pardon, avoid terrible bloodshed and hopefully reach some kind of agreement, was the lesser of the two evils.

Presumably Warwick hoped a pardon would also bring about the release of the many gentlemen held captive by the rebels. After the parley the Herald returned to St Stephen's Gate and was escorted by 40 rebels 'very pleasant and friendly' through the city to Bishop Bridge. Near here a large crowd had gathered from the rebel camp and many greeted the Herald with shouts of 'God save the King'. They were offered a general pardon, Kett excepted, but when the Herald condemned their behaviour and announced that such 'vile and horrible company' must accept the pardon or else be crushed with great force, their mood soon changed. Some of the rebels may well have been intimidated but it seems many were angered by these words and said the pardon was a deception which would not be honoured; others became threatening and said the Herald was not genuine but an agent of the gentry.

A 'vile boy' is killed and hopes of peace are lost

At this point Kett appeared and defused a tense situation by leading the frightened Herald a little way off to read the pardon again, so that others could hear. Unfortunately Kett's assertion of his personal authority and efforts to calm the situation were fatally undermined, by the unexpected behaviour of a boy who turned his back to the Herald and bared his buttocks. Such an act of bravado so angered the Herald's bodyguard that he shot the boy dead.

It was a critical moment, for until this incident the rebels were fairly calm; now there was uproar. Some saw it as an act of treachery and evidence that the 'gentlemen may kill and beat us all down at their pleasure'. Others who could not have seen the incident, heard rumours spreading through the crowd and shouted, 'our men are killed by the riverside'. Amid the tumult Kett led the Herald away and was going it seems, to meet Warwick to try and negotiate a settlement which perhaps would include Warwick's personal guarantee of the pardon for the rebels, but which he knew would exclude himself.

However, as Kett and the Herald rode away to meet Warwick, another band of rebels surrounded them and shouted 'Whither away, whither away Mr Kett? If you go, we will go with you, and with you will live and die'. What a dilemma faced Kett! He must have been torn between responding to the display of loyalty and affection by his men and the need to negotiate with Warwick to avoid further bloodshed. At the same time the Herald was concerned only with his own safety and told Kett to 'stay this concourse and tumult'. Reluctantly it seems, Kett was persuaded to remain with his men. Another crucial moment had passed and another opportunity to find a way out of the impasse into which the rebels had become inexorably drawn, vanished with the sound of horses hooves as the Herald galloped back to the Earl of Warwick.

Warwick's army occupies Norwich- 24 August

Facing the inevitable attack by the royal army, the rebels closed all the city gates and manned the walls. At this point Steward and Aldrich managed to escape, thereby disassociating themselves from complicity in Kett's Rebellion.

Warwick's soldiers quickly forced an entry at St. Stephen's Gate and the Brasen Doors. In the street fighting nearby many rebels were killed and 49 others were summarily hanged later in the day in the market place. An entry in the City Chamberlain's Accounts records that 8 pence was paid to 'make a pair of gallows' and 3 shillings and 9 pence 'for the charges of burying 49 men that were hanged at the cross in the Market and for making pits and carrying them'. Another entry refers to the mending of a ladder, 'that was broken at the cross with hanging of men'.

Warwick's main army entered Norwich at St Benedict's Gate and marched directly to the market place which became its military base. However, the army's baggage train and artillery got lost near Tombland, turning down Bishopgate by mistake. Here a group of rebels gleefully captured the guns and supplies and dragged them up to their camp. Althought Captain Drury was sent in pursuit, he was too late to retrieve the guns but killed some rebels in the skirmish.

The rebels launch a counter-attack

Cheered by the capture of the enemy's cannons, the rebels prepared to ambush and attack Warwick's men in the maze of streets and alleys between Tombland and the market place. Three companies of rebels used the churches of St Michael at Plea, St Simon and St Jude and St Andrew's as bases, while others assembled 'by the Elm and about the Hill next the corner of the building late the Black Friars, in battle array'.

St. Andrew's Hall

In the desperate street fighting some of Warwick's soldiers and a number of gentlemen were killed. However, Drury's arrival on the scene halted the rebels near St Andrew's Hall. Their 'mighty force of arrows' now received 'such a terrible volley of shot as if it had been a storm of hail, and put them all to flight'. Gunfire had won the day against archers. After this bloody engagment, many rebels fled through the cathedral grounds to the safety of Mousehold; others less fortunate were slain where they lay, hiding in the churchyards. Although Drury's men sustained heavy casualties over 300 rebels died too. Warwick had been shaken by the resourcefulness of Kett's men who also captured more guns, but the full weight of his power had proved enough to drive the rebels back and by evening Warwick was still in control of Norwich.

By sunset stalemate had been reached. The rebels were secure on their hillside camp but Warwick was master of Norwich, a situation not unlike that on 31 July when Northampton had arrived. However, Kett could not afford to be shut out of Norwich for long because it was vital for supplies to his camp. On the other hand

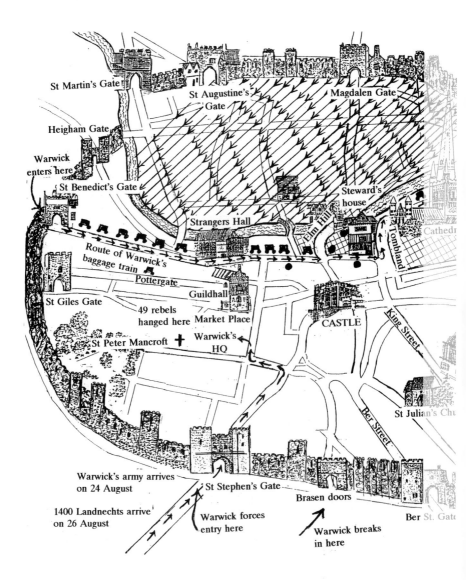

St Martin's Gate

St Augustine's Gate

Magdalen Gate

Heigham Gate

Warwick enters here

St Benedict's Gate

Strangers Hall

Steward's house

Elm Hill

Tombland

Cathedr

Route of Warwick's baggage train

Pottergate

St Giles Gate

Guildhall

49 rebels hanged here

Market Place

CASTLE

King Street

St Peter Mancroft

Warwick's HQ

Ber Street

St Julian's Chu

Warwick's army arrives on 24 August

St Stephen's Gate

Brasen doors

1400 Landnechts arrive on 26 August

Warwick forces entry here

Warwick breaks in here

Ber St. Gate

54

THE STRUGGLE FOR NORWICH
24-26 AUGUST

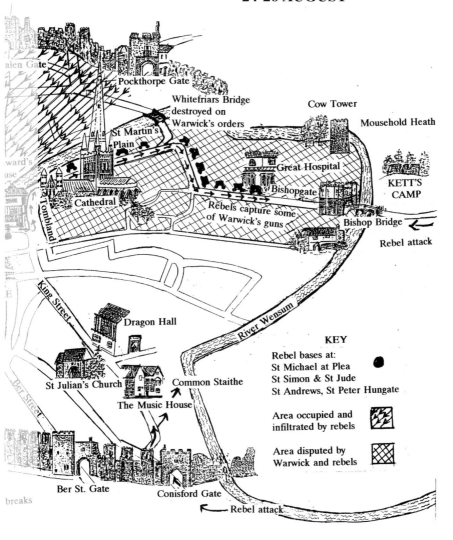

Pockthorpe Gate

Whitefriars Bridge destroyed on Warwick's orders

Cow Tower

Mousehold Heath

St Martin's Plain

Great Hospital

KETT'S CAMP

Cathedral

Bishopgate

Rebels capture some of Warwick's guns

Bishop Bridge

Rebel attack

Tombland

King Street

River Wensum

Dragon Hall

KEY

Rebel bases at:
St Michael at Plea
St Simon & St Jude
St Andrews, St Peter Hungate

St Julian's Church

Common Staithe

The Music House

Area occupied and infiltrated by rebels

Area disputed by Warwick and rebels

Ber St. Gate

Conisford Gate

Rebel attack

if Warwick could hold on for a few days, the rebels would have to come off Mousehold and thus give Warwick a chance to face them on open ground.

The rebels try to recapture Norwich - 25 August

This was a critical day in the struggle for control of Norwich. It began with an artillery attack by the rebels during which Miles, Kett's chief gunner damaged Cow Tower and Bishopgate Bridge. But the cannons lacked the range and power to do decisive damage and few of the rebels had the expertise needed to fire their captured guns.

Cow Tower

Warwick recognised the importance of Bishop Bridge sending reinforcements to the area while making his own headquarters at Steward's house in Tombland and leaving troop rerserves in the market place.

Meanwhile, Kett's men broke in at Conisford Gate and fired houses in King Street but Warwick refused to risk men to put out the flames in case he was outflanked. Another rebel attack broke through the walls between Pockthorpe and Magdalen Gates occupying the area north of the Wensum. They were driven back but at some cost to Warwick whose casualties included two gentlemen and three of Drury's gunners.

However, many in Norwich fearing further destruction of the city, urged Warwick to withdraw and meet the rebel army on more favourable ground outside the walls. But to do this would mean dividing his forces, for some would need to stay behind to defend the city, while Kett would still hold the high ground. In fact Warwick decided to hold the city and said he would not depart 'but would deliver it or leave his life', demanding the citizens unite with him against Kett or face destruction. This seems to have

56

convinced them and they readily offered food and accommodation to his troops. To emphasise his authority in Norwich, Warwick placed his arms, the 'bear and ragged staff' on Steward's house, and urged that the four bridges which joined the northern part of Norwich to the heart of the city, Coslany, Blackfriars, Fye and Whitefriars be destroyed, to check rebel infiltration. Protests by the citizens saved all but Whitefriars Bridge.

Fye Bridge

Warwick's military tactics were sound, for if he could hold Norwich for a little longer thus cutting off the flow of vital supplies to Mousehold, the rebels would be forced to leave their camp and face him in open battle, a situation which would clearly favour the royal army.

For the remainder of the day the fighting was furious. It was a close-run thing, but Warwick kept the rebels at bay. However, Kett's men were running out of supplies and time; gradually the scales tipped against them as the exhausted rebels had no reinforcements to call on, whereas Warwick knew 1400 fresh mercenaries would be arriving next day.

The Lansknechts arrive - 26 August

While Warwick was enjoying the hospitality of the Maid's Head, a volley of shot announced the arrival of 1400 German mercenaries. They had an awesome reputation and were among the best troops in Europe. Originally intended for the Scottish campaign they provided Warwick with a decisive advantage, and greatly boosted his confidence. Renowned for their discipline and power the Lansknechts were superbly equipped; apart from armour their weapons included arquebueses (hand guns), pikes and swords and they also had cavalry and artillery. The news that such powerful reinforcements now faced them must have increased anxiety among the rebels.

We can only speculate about Kett's thoughts at this point. He had for some days been swept along by events and must have realised now that a fearful outcome was likely. He had come a long way since leaving the quiet pastures of Wymondham where he had courageously stood up for the cause of justice. Now this unlikely leader of the most dramatic and well organised demonstration against injustice in Tudor England, faced the prospect of a bloody encounter with a large force of professional soldiers. It was not what he had planned or wanted; indeed he had tried hard to avoid such an outcome.

The rebels break camp

On the evening of 26 August the rebels made the fateful decision to leave their camp. There were many reasons for doing so. Firstly, they had been camped there for over six weeks, and though this was a triumph of organisation by Kett, conditions must have become very difficult, especially in the last few days. They were exhausted and emotionally distraught, having lost many comrades. Many of the agricultural elements among the men were concerned about the harvest. But the most compelling reason to leave their position of security on Mousehold was that Warwick had succeeded in cutting their supply lines so that no victuals could reach the camp. Having failed to dislodge Warwick from Norwich, the rebels now faced the added hardship of serious shortages of essential supplies. It had become necessary to force the issue and come down and face the enemy on open ground. Some rebels may have been spurred on by a misguided belief in an ancient prophecy:

The country gnoffes, Hob, Dick and Hick,
With clubs and clouted shoon,
Shall fill the vale of Dussindale
With slaughtered bodies soon

This led them to suppose they would win a great victory and many of the gentry would be slain in the vale of Dussindale. Morale may well have been still quite high - the rebels had enjoyed two victories before Warwick arrived and they had given him a real fright too. Some may have felt they could now avenge the loss of comrades in previous battles.

Kett was probably not so optimistic and was under pressure to act. His sense of gloom may have increased when a snake leapt out of a tree into the bosom of his wife, which was seen as a bad omen by many. It is the only reference to Mrs Kett in the story. Perhaps Kett had arranged for her to be with him on that last day before the camp moved off to the battle, because he feared the worst.

The rebels prepare for the final battle

Under cover of darkness the rebels left Mousehold taking what ordnance and munitions they had. They wanted to draw up their battle position and defences to the best advantage before Warwick could move against them. When they reached their chosen ground, they dug ditches, erected stakes and put up barricades of waggons placing their cannons around them.

The rebels placed the manacled gentlemen prisoners in front of their army to form a human shield. Many lived in hope of a great victory, in part due to their belief in the ancient prophecies, another one of which said:

'The heedless men within the dale
Shall there be slain both great and small'.

However, the rebels did not seem to consider the possibility that the rhymes may have alluded to the fate of their own class, the 'country gnoffes' and that the slaughtered bodies might be themselves rather than the gentry.

Dussindale - disaster for the 'country gnoffes'

Now that Warwick's troops could fight on open ground rather than being fettered by the Norwich streets, the outcome of the battle was never in doubt; the rebels were doomed to defeat.

On the morning of 27 August the royal army left the city by St Martin's Gate turning right 'straight towards the enemy' (Holinshed). The English infantry were left in Norwich as a garrison and also because Warwick knew they would not relish the prospect of killing their own kind. As his troops approached the rebel position he sent forward a small party with the offer of a pardon to all except the leaders, a final attempt to avoid a battle and also a ploy to secure the safe release of Kett's prisoners. The pardon was again rejected and so all who fought, were acting treasonably and could face the death penalty if they survived the battle. That the rebels refused a pardon yet again, is partly because they did not believe it would be honoured, but it is in no small way a tribute to the leadership and the spirit in the rebel force.

Warwick began the attack with a cannonade to 'soften up' the enemy. Then Miles, Kett's chief gunner shot the royal standard-bearer and brought down his horse. Doubtless infuriated, Warwick ordered an infantry advance involving Drury's arquebusiers and the Lansknechts. The power and discipline of a withering volley of shot followed by the 'push of pike', broke the front rank of the rebels and some began to retreat in disorder. In the ensuing chaos many of Kett's prisoners escaped though 'some were slain by the Lansknechts that knew not what they were'(Holinshed). Further heavy arquebus fire poured into the rebel lines. Then a cavalry advance completed the collapse of the rebel formation. Many fled like scattered sheep in various directions in confusion and terror pursued by marauding cavalry, the gentry of East Anglia. What followed was not unlike a hunt, as many terrified peasants tried to seek a hiding place or pleaded for mercy from a vengeful gentry. Holinshed records that the horsemen 'slew them down in heaps even as they overtook them'. It was sheer carnage yet some rebels bravely resisted in desperate skirmishes during the general rout. Ill-armed and poorly equipped groups fought bravely in a few isolated rallies. One group decided it was better to die manfully in battle than be killed like sheep as they ran. Hastily erecting a barricade of carts and stakes they prepared to make a 'last stand'. However, Warwick perhaps impressed by their bravery and anxious to avoid further bloodshed

BATTLE OF DUSSINDALE 27 AUGUST 1549

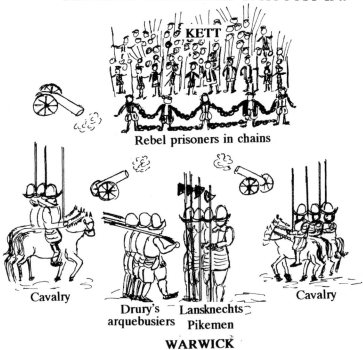

Rebel prisoners in chains

Cavalry

Drury's   Lansknechts
arquebusiers   Pikemen

WARWICK

STAGES IN THE BATTLE

1. Royal cannons 'soften up' rebel formation
2. Miles, chief rebel gunner kills royal standard-bearer
3. Volley of shot by the arquebusiers
4. 'Push of pike' breaks rebel formation
5. Cavalry charge completes break-up of rebel lines
6. Rebels flee in disorder pursued by cavalry
7. 'Last stand' by some rebels who surrender when offered Warwick's pardon
8. Cavalry chase and kill fleeing rebels

offered a pardon. But only when he appeared in person to confirm the pardon did this embattled remnant of Kett's army lay down its arms.

By late afternoon the uneven contest was over. Kett had left the scene before the end, demoralised. Warwick had lost perhaps over 200 men including eight gentlemen but some 3,000 rebels lay dead after the battle of Dussindale.

Where was Dussindale ?

There has been much speculation about the location of the battlefield. Early writers have placed it at various points to the north of Norwich between the Sprowston and Drayton Roads. However, while Anne Carter was researching the history of Postwick in the 1980s, she discovered a Dussings Deale on a map of the area. Documentary evidence indicates the existence of a valley of this name which is located on the borders of Thorpe, Postwick and Great Plumstead, near Green Lane South.

This location is nearly three miles from Mount Surrey but Sotherton says the prophetic dale was 'not past a myle of and somewhat more' and the site north of Norwich is just over a mile from the rebel camp. Holinshed says that Warwick marched out of St Martin's Gate 'straight towards the enemy' having had intelligence of the direction of the rebels route from their camp, from 'ye watche' on the cathedral steeple. This suggests a location northwards rather than well to the east of Norwich. The indictment of Kett says that Dussindale was 'in the parishes of Thorpe and Sprowston'.

The subject remains fascinatingly elusive. If the early writers are correct the rebels would have met their fate in in the low ground west of Aylsham Road or been driven out of Sprowston into Thorpe where some may well have died in the Green Lane area.

We will probably never know the whole story of that fateful day, but it is reasonable to conjecture that in the course of their chaotic flight from the cavalry, the rebels scattered in several directions and that some did indeed end up in Thorpe, while others may have met their fate in the low ground north west of Norwich. The fighting sprawled over a large area; Blomefield says the 'chase' of the fleeing rebels was over three or four miles. The key point is that the battle ended Kett's Rebellion and the high hopes of its leader that a demonstration against injustice would bring about reform in Norfolk.

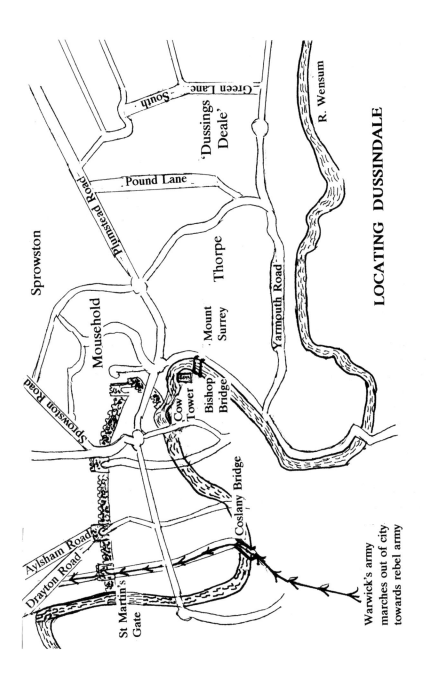

LOCATING DUSSINDALE

Sprowston

Mousehold

Thorpe

Mount Surrey

'Dussings Deale'

Green Lane South

Pound Lane

Plumstead Road

Sprowston Road

Aylsham Road

Drayton Road

St Martin's Gate

Cow Tower

Bishop Bridge

Coslany Bridge

Yarmouth Road

R. Wensum

Warwick's army marches out of city towards rebel army

63

AFTERMATH OF REBELLION

Kett is captured - 28 August

Once the outcome of the battle became clear, Kett left the scene and rode off in a northerly direction, presumably alone. What his plans were we can only guess, but on reaching Swannington in an exhausted state, he sought refuge in a barn on an isolated farm some way out of the village. Despite the secluded spot, he was seen and recognised by some men unloading hay. They took him to a Mr Riches and though left guarded by a young child for a time, he made no attempt to escape because he was mentally and physically exhausted by the pressures of the previous days. He was given food and allowed to rest while word was sent to Warwick. Next morning, 28 August, soldiers arrived to arrest Kett and bring him back to Norwich. Over five months later on 3 February 1550 the Privy Council ordered that '20 shillings was paid to him that first apprehended Kett the rebel'.

Reprisals after the battle of Dussindale

The morning after Dussindale many of the rebels who had survived the battle were executed. The first victims were nine of the rebel leaders including Miles and Fulke who were hanged at the Oak of Reformation. They were then drawn and quartered and their heads fixed on tops of towers about the city. Further hangings took place outside Magdalen Gate of perhaps another 200 rebels, a customary procedure by a military commander after the defeat of a rebel force to deter further disorder. There would have been even more ritual hangings after Dussindale if vengeful gentry had had their way. However, Warwick showed some moderation and urged mercy, while reminding the gentry that their bloodlust was in danger of causing a labour shortage when he said, 'Would you be ploughmen yourselves and harrow your own land?'

Norwich gives thanks for Kett's defeat

Next day, 29 August, large numbers of Norwich citizens and gentry attended a service of thanksgiving in the church of St Peter Mancroft where the congregation gave humble thanks for delivering the city from the rebel Kett and his followers. Thereafter Warwick's arms the bear and ragged staff, appeared at various places in Norwich in honour of the man who was seen by many as the saviour of the city from great danger and peril.

St. Peter Mancroft

Norwich decides to do the same each year

In September the City decided that a service should commemorate the victory over Kett at Dussindale on 27 August each year, 'to have the same day always in our remembrance for ever'. Such was the desire to perpetuate the event in the memory that the city ordered that a sermon be preached on the subject once a year. This practice was still being followed in 1667, and as late as 1728 the event was celebrated as a festival for the relief of the city from the rebels. Thus was salt rubbed into the wounds of defeat, death and despair which visited so many Norfolk families in the summer of 1549.

Warwick tackles problems in Norwich

Warwick remained in Norwich until 7 September to deal with the many problems which faced the city authorities in the days following Kett's defeat. After their victory, Warwick's troops were rewarded with beer in the market place and then allowed to sell any 'prey' or booty they had been authorised to take from the defeated rebels. Then Warwick supervised the gruesome task of hanging rebel prisoners and arranging for the bodies to be buried or burnt.

Many citizens claimed compensation for damaged property or expenses for services rendered during the rebellion. Then there were accusations by the gentry and disputes about property to consider. Warwick could only make a start in tackling such problems but he did lay down some guidelines for the local courts to follow. During this period Warwick and his son Robert Dudley, probably visited Intwood Hall and Stanfield Hall where Robert met and began the unfortunate courtship of Amy Robsart whom he later married. However, she died in suspicious circumstances in 1560, when Dudley was Queen Elizabeth's favourite.

Clearing up Norwich after Warwick's departure

When Warwick's army with Robert and William Kett in chains, finally set off for London on 7 September, there was probably widespread relief in Norwich. Apart from the earlier military engagements, the city had endured 12,000 soldiers quartered within its boundaries for two weeks. So began a big clear-up of accumulated rubbish. The market place, the main base for Warwick's army and the cathedral grounds and cloisters which were used by his cavalry much to the dismay of some citizens, were the first priorities. Ten labourers took over three weeks to remove 248 cart-loads of rubbish from the market square, while the rubbish around the Guildhall and inside the prison area kept one man busy for 11 days.

When normality returned to the Norwich market, five former stallholders were missing. Thomas Toly a butcher, had been 'hanged as a traitor' and Edmond Ferebye, John King, John Hylle and John Olivar, former rebels, had fled after the rebellion and did not return. It is a reminder that Kett had followers in the city as well as in the countryside.

Market Cross Norwich

Buildings damaged during the rebellion

Apart from cleaning streets and removing rubbish there was inevitably damage to some buildings in the city. Repairs were necessary but the surprising thing is that the damage was not greater. The view that the city was on the point of destruction is a gross exaggeration. The presence of soldiers may well have been responsible for damage to St Andrew's Hall, used as a provisions store by Warwick and for stabling purposes.

Whitefriars Bridge destroyed on Warwick's advice was rebuilt and Fye Bridge needed repair. Some city gates were damaged during the fighting, including Pockthorpe, Magdalen, St Augustine's, St Stephen's, Conesford and Bishop Bridge Gate; Cow Tower also needed minor repairs.

The rebels did not deliberately damage church buildings and few were seriously affected by the fighting. Some private houses were damaged during the turmoil, especially in Bishopgate and King Street and along the common staithe, from where burnt corn and rubbish were removed.

The Town Close whose hedges were pulled down when the rebels first came to Norwich, was re-ditched and hedged by three men bringing 24 loads of thorns from Hethel, a job which took them 17 days.

The cost of Kett's Rebellion was considerable, but most of the outlay went on paying and feeding soldiers, providing services for the royal commanders and their entrourages and settling expenses claimed by civic leaders and others, rather than on paying for repairs resulting from wanton destruction by the rebels.

Kett in prison and on trial - 9 September to 26 November

On 9 September, while Norwich was returning to normal Robert and his brother William began a period of imprisonment in the Tower of London. William was presumably captured at Dussindale or arrested shortly after. He seems to have been treated more leniently than Robert, for according to the list of prisoners confined at the time, William 'goeth at large in the Tower'.

On 23 November, six judges were appointed to deal with the Ketts; the trial took place on 26 November. Because of their 'felonious, malicious and traitorous' conduct and for 'exciting sedition, rebellion and insurrection between the King and his faithful subjects', both Ketts were found guilty of treason though the details in the lengthy indictment are in parts confusing and in conflict with other known evidence. No evidence survives of any statement Kett may have made at the trial, or whether he was allowed to see his family.

The position of William Kett in the rebellion

William's more lenient treatment in the Tower of London, has led some to suggest that, had Somerset not fallen from power, he would have been pardoned. There is no evidence however, for this view and one chronicler's description of him as being popular because of 'his desperate hardiness' suggests William was of strong character - not the sort to meekly submit or adopt a low profile during the struggle. The view that William played little part in the commotion is not borne out by the indictment, which reveals William's total support for his brother during the rebellion and furthermore, states that he 'gave comfort, aid and counsel to the traitorous designs of Robert Kett to excite sedition, rebellion, and insurrection between the King and his subjects'.

Another allegation levelled against William is that he submitted to Northampton and was then sent to persuade his brother to do likewise. But William changed his mind and dissuaded Robert from accepting a pardon. On returning to the camp, William was also reminded of the vast size of the rebel army in comparison to the relatively small royal contingent, which would be easy to overcome. This version of events is intriguing but there is nothing to substantiate it.

The indictment cited William as being equally guilty of treason as Robert in rallying men under arms at the camp and subverting their obedience to the King. Although there is little reference to William's role in the near-contemporary accounts, there is no reason to suppose that he was anything other than a loyal and active supporter of his brother. Why William was given freer rein in the Tower than Robert remains a mystery.

Sentence and execution of the Ketts - 7 December

After the trial both men were sentenced to be hanged at Tyburn, then while still alive they would be cut down, their entrails burnt, their heads cut off and their bodies quartered. However it was then decided that the executions should take place in Norfolk. On 29 November Sir Edmund Windham Sheriff of Norfolk, was made responsible for this and he brought them back to Norwich where on 1 December they were placed in fetters in the Guildhall dungeon.

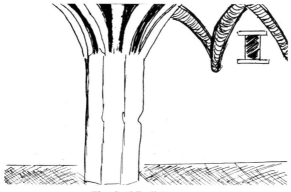

The Guildhall Dungeon

The executions took place on 7 December. Robert Kett was taken in chains on an open hurdle to Norwich Castle where he was hanged from the walls after being hauled up alive from the ground. His body was left to rot, 'for winter store'. On the same day William Kett was hanged in chains at Wymondham from the west tower of the Abbey church which he and his brother had loved and served so well. In referring to William's execution, a chronicler recorded that it was 'not without murmuring that that church dedicated to the service of God..... should be made a place of execution'.

Before Kett's execution, anonymous threats had been made in the hope of forcing the authorities to change their minds. One of these warned, 'It (the hanging) should cost a 1,000 men their lives'. Another predicted, 'You'll see as great a camp on Mousehold as ever there was, before Christmas or in the Spring, and men will come from the Lord Protector's country to strengthen him'. This was a vain hope, for Somerset had been sent to the Tower himself in October, his policies being blamed for the disorders of 1549 by his rival Warwick.

The consequences of Kett's Rebellion

Some 4,000 died as a result of the rebellion, most of whom were of course rebels, though 350 were killed on the government side. In financial terms the cost of the Western Rebellion and the Norfolk Rising combined was £27,330 7s 6d. The impact on Norwich was considerable; however, the dislocation of trade was due to the uncertainty of the times rather than direct disruption of commercial life in the city by the rebels. On the few occasions

69

when the rebels fought in the streets, it was against the soldiers sent against them not the people of Norwich. Considering that Kett's men dominated or occupied the city for over six weeks, the damage to buildings and economic life in general was relatively small and there was no sustained looting or wanton destruction.

There was much public sympathy for Kett and his cause after the defeat at Dussindale, as illustrated by this heartfelt statement by a parish clerk of a Norwich church that, 'There are too many gentlemen in England by 500', while another said, 'I did well in keeping Kett's camp and thought nothing but well of Kett. He trusted to see a new day, for such as I'.

After Kett's execution much hostility was directed against Warwick whose arms, the bear and ragged staff, had been placed on gates and buildings in the city. This offended some who said the arms should be 'plucked down'. In February 1550, one man said, 'it was not meet to have any more Kings than one' and 'Kett should be plucked down from the top of the castle'. Another warned with excessive optimism, that the 500 Mousehold men who were abroad fighting for the King 'will be here again by midsummer'.

Despite such sentiments, the gentry consolidated its grip in the countryside; Hales the champion of the anti-enclosure movement was discredited, Somerset's Enclosure Commission collapsed and the enclosure movement continued unchecked. Organised opposition to enclosure was made a treasonable offence by Parliament, and Robert Crowley echoed the determination of the gentry to maintain their sway, when he wrote in 1550, 'And if they once stir again or do but once cluster together, we will hang them at their own doors'.

The main political result of the rebellion was the fall of Somerset, executed for treason in 1552, and the rise of the Earl of Warwick who became the most powerful man in England until his life also ended on the scaffold in 1553. When Edward VI died in 1553, Warwick tried to prevent the accession of Mary Tudor by proclaiming Lady Jane Grey Queen. But Mary had fled to Kenninghall, then to Framlingham Castle. She received much popular support and Norwich was among the first cities to proclaim Mary Queen. She was supported in Norfolk partly because of her legitimacy and alleged promises to respect the recent religious changes but moreso, because of bitter memories of Warwick and his treatment of the rebels in 1549; thus did the 'poore commons' gain revenge on the victor of Dussindale. Warwick soon became isolated in the wave of support for Mary; he was arrested, sent to the Tower and executed on 22 August 1553.

Another result of the rebellion was the Crown's decision to appoint a Lord Lieutenant for each county, responsible for raising and maintaining militias to deal with disorder. It was the first step towards the creation of a standing army.

But the rebellion lived on in the memory of the lower orders in Norfolk; for later generations, Kett's Camp became a symbol of the continued struggle for social justice.

The impact of the rebellion on the Kett family

The properties of Robert and William were forfeited to the Crown after the rebellion, but any setback to the fortunes of the Kett family proved temporary. None of the family suffered judicial reprisals after Dussindale, evidence that they were not implicated in the rebellion. Robert's eldest son William, was later restored to part of his father's property but not Gunvile Manor, which was granted in 1550 to Thomas Audley. He was also granted the lands of Westwode forfeited by his uncle William, which eventually went to the Great Hospital in Norwich (1571).

After 1549, many of the Kett family continued to lead honourable and prosperous lives like their ancestors. For example Richard Kett, Robert's third son a churchwarden at Beeston, bequeathed in 1601 some tenements for the use and benefit of the poor. He also left 20 marks to the church for repairs to the steeple. His funeral was attended by many friends and large numbers of the poor. In 1588 he had given £25 for the defence of the country at the time of the Spanish Armada.

Gonville Hall based on an 18th Century painting

71

Kett's second son Loye, who lived at Crownthorpe left 20 shillings to the blind, lame and very aged of Wymondham and £50 each to two of his grandaughters. George Kett, the youngest son who lived at Shotesham made bequests to the poor of Shotesham, Wymondham, Framingham Earl and Poringland. Thomas Kett, Robert's younger brother left 10 shillings to repair the highway from Wymondham to Norwich. Such bequests displayed the same public spiritedness and compassion that Robert showed during the Norfolk Rising.

CONCLUSION - SOME THOUGHTS AND SPECULATIONS

Before Kett became the leader of the Norfolk Rising, he was respected and respectable, a prosperous and secure family man, active in the church and a pillar of the Wymondham community. He had everything to gain from enclosure, investing in property at a time when the land market was buoyant and remaining law-abiding. So why did he stand up, speak out and risk all ? A variety of factors have been suggested; social conscience, rivalry with Flowerdew, class feeling, a conviction that the 'good duke' would respond to a self-evidently just cause. Whatever the explanation, his action seems to have been considered rather than impulsive though his assumption of leadership was as unlikely and unexpected as it was remarkable and inspirational. The enigma of Kett explains his enduring appeal.

Kett was a thoughtful, caring man whose conscience, an amalgam of his religious upbringing and values he had imbibed from the guilds, was troubled by what he saw around him, especially the callous disregard by many of the great landowners in Norfolk for the plight of the poor. Here was no ambitious opportunist driven by personal advancement and self-interest, but a man who was humane and moderate. No violence was done against his enemies except in battle. His camp was devoid of the brutal methods employed by his social superiors and restrained by administrative order and a belief in 'good governance' and 'justice'.

Kett has been seen as a paradoxical figure; a loyal Roman Catholic and a champion of the 'new religion', an encloser of land and the leader of a campaign against it, a pillar of his local community who became a rebel for a principle and put himself outside the law, a successful and prosperous yeoman farmer and businessman who became the champion of the less fortunate. Yet despite these apparent contradictions, the story of Kett's Rebellion reveals a man who was flexible, pragmatic and open-minded enough to move with the times and strong enough to make a stand for something he believed was right.

Kett was no ordinary rebel for though bold, resolute and charismatic, he was also shrewd, positive and willing to negotiate. He did not threaten the government but appealed to the King to reform local corruption in Norfolk. He had no quarrel with Norwich, neither did he make any serious attempt to spread the rebellion; his camp was administered with restraint and dignity. He wanted reform not revolution and was neither socialist nor radical. He wanted not a new order but the restoration of a modified more stable society which he thought was imperilled by grasping landowners and lawyers. The Requests would have checked the tide of nascent capitalism and greed. The camp on Mousehold was a demonstration not only of a reformed state, but evidence that the lower orders were just as capable of managing their affairs as the ruling elite which monopolised power.

The rebellion came about when relations between the ruling class and the common people in Norfolk had reached their lowest ebb. Kett however, stood for stability, just laws and 'a quietness in the realm'. To the lower orders he became an iconic figure who gave hope to the poorest and disadvantaged as well as those who already had a small stake in society. He led a rainbow coalition of the comfortably-off and the common man, the 'haves' and the 'have-nots', the skilled artisan in the town and the humble labourer in the village, the tenant farmer and the rural poor. Kett's Rebellion was a rising of the town as well as the countryside.

But the high hopes of his followers who were given a glimpse of a 'better day' on Mousehold came to nought. Over 4,000 died, either butchered at Dussindale, killed in the blood-spattered streets and lanes of Norwich, or in cold terror on the gallows. Such a tragic outcome was of course inevitable.

The rebellion had failed because Warwick's resources were greater and his tactics decisive. Also by late August Kett must have been completely exhausted by the strain of the past six weeks and was probably losing heart. However, it appears that he was working for a peaceful outcome at the end, and it is is worth remembering that the final bloody battle may well have been avoided, but for the impudence of a 'rude boy' and the impetuous response of one of the Herald's bodyguards. Thereafter, Kett realised the game was up and that neither the superstitious beliefs of many of his followers, nor remaining stubbornly on the heights of Mousehold, could avert disaster.

Some have called the rebellion a glorious failure or lost cause, in which people have taken a romantic interest. But Kett was much more than a summertime rebel enjoying the 'camping time'. Although the collapse of the rebellion was rapid, the personality of Kett – with whose name it remained inseparably linked – ensured that the spirit of the rising lived on. Kett may have become involved in the rebellion because of circumstances, but his leadership gave impetus to the cause, the value of which would eventually be recognised by a more enlightened age.

It was a time of turmoil and uncertainty in English history. New political, religious, social and economic forces were transforming a society which had changed little for centuries. Above all, the old medieval order was being overtaken by the tide of commercialism and a money-based economy. Kett could not of course stop such a tide. However, in a time of tumult, he drew attention to the everyday grievances and concerns of the thousands who were excluded from any control over or say in, the conditions of life they could only endure. Such a stand attracted many to his camp on Mousehold Heath. In exposing the consequences of the new forces, which he believed threatened economic and social justice, he was only acting according to his conscience.

Kett may have been vanquished at Dussindale, vilified by the State and cruelly hanged from Norwich Castle's walls, but later generations have vindicated him. Such an unlikely figure may have died a traitor by the standards of his day, but he had courageously led a struggle against injustice; for that he will always be remembered.

"Be brave then, for your captain is brave and vows reformation" Henry IV Part 2

APPENDICES

List of Kett's fellow 'Governors' and the 24 Hundreds they represented at the Mousehold Camp

Forehoe	-	Robert Kett, Thomas Rolf, William Kett
North Greenhoe	-	Edmund Famingham, William Tyddle
South Erpingham	-	Reynold Thurston, John Wolsey
E. Flegg & W.Flegg	-	Simon English, William Peck
Launditch	-	George Blomefield, William Harrison
Eynesford	-	Edmund Belys, Robert Sendall
Humbleyard	-	Thomas Prick, Henry Hodgekins
North Erpingham	-	Richard Bevis, William Doughty
Taverham	-	Thomas Garrod, William Peter
Brothercross	-	Robert Manson, Robert Ede
Blofield	-	John Spregey, Eli Hull
Walsham	-	John Kitball, Thomas Clarke
Tunstead	-	John Harper, Richard Lyon
Happing	-	Edward Joy, Thomas Clock
Henstead	-	William Mowe, Thomas Halling
Holt	-	John Vossell, Valentine Moore
Loddon & Clavering	-	Robert Lerold, Richard Ward
South Greenhoe	-	Edward Bird, Thomas Tuddenham
Mitford	-	Simon Newell, William Howling
Freebridge (Lynn)	-	William Heydon, Thomas Jacker
Gallow	-	Robert Cott, John Oxwick
Depwade	-	William Brown, Simond Sendall
(Suffolk)	-	Richard Wright

Select list from the 29 Rebel Requests

We pray your grace that no lord of the manor shall common upon the commons

We pray that rivers may be free and common to all men for fishing and passage

We pray that all bond men may be made free, for God made all free with his precious bloodshedding

We pray that rede ground and meadow ground may be at such price as they were in the first year of King Henry VII

We pray that no man under the degree of a knight or esquire keep a dove house, except it hath been of an ancient custom

We pray that all freeholders and copyholders may take the profits of all commons, and the lords not to common nor take profit of the same

75

We pray that no lord, squire nor gentleman do graze nor feed any bullocks or sheep if he may spend £40 a year by his lands, but only for the provision of his house

We pray that priests or vicars that be not able to preach and set forth the word of God to his parishioners may be thereby put from his benefice, and the parishioners there to choose another, or else the patron or lord of the town (to do so)

We pray that every proprietary parson or vicar having a benefice of £10 or more by year, shall either by themselves, or by some other person teach poor men's children of their parish the book called the catechism and the primer

We pray your grace to take all liberty of lete into your own hands, whereby all men may quietly enjoy their commons with profit (lete was a local manor court which the rebels wanted to be controlled by the Crown rather than the local lord)

We pray that those your officers, which have offended your grace and your commons, and are so proved by the complaint of your poor commons, do give unto these poor men so assembled 4d every day so long as they have remained there.

CHIEF FIGURES IN THE STORY OF KETT'S REBELLION

Rebels

Robert Kett	-	tanner, yeoman farmer, leader of the rebellion
William Kett	-	grazier, mercer, loyal to Kett
Miles	-	chief gunner in rebel army
Fulke	-	butcher, killed Lord Sheffield on St Martin's Plain
Flotman	-	led a group who rejected Northampton's pardon

Citizens of Norwich

Thomas Codd	-	mayor, captured by Kett, later released, signed the Requests
Thomas Aldrich	-	senior alderman, signed the Requests
Augustine Steward	-	deputy mayor, entertained the royal commanders at his house in Tombland
Henry Bacon	-	deputy sheriff, worked with Steward
Tom Coniers	-	minister at St Martin's Church, and chaplain at Kett's camp
Robert Watson	-	a 'new preacher', associated with Kett's camp
Leonard Sotherton	-	merchant, sought help from London
Nicholas Sotherton	-	merchant, wrote an account of the rebellion

County authorities

Master Hobart	-	enclosing landlord at Morley, whose fences were destroyed by rioters
John Flowerdew	-	lawyer, landowner, personal rival of Kett
John Green	-	of Wilby manor whose fences were destroyed by rioters
John Corbet	-	gentlemen-lawyer, whose house and dovecote were destroyed by the rebels
Sir Roger Wodehouse	-	of Kimberley Hall, taken prisoner by the rebels when he tried to disperse them
Sir Edmund Knyvett	-	of Buckenham Castle, tried to break up the rebel camp at Hingham
Sir Edmund Windham	-	High Sheriff of Norfolk, tried to disperse the rebels and was later responsible for Kett's custody before his execution
Sir Thomas Clere & Sir Thomas Woodhouse	-	organised defence of Yarmouth against the rebels
Sir William Paston	-	of Caister, sent two cannons to Norwich

Norfolk gentry families involved in helping to suppress the rebellion included: Bedingfeld, Townshend, Cornwallis, Warner, Southwell, Parker.

Representatives of the central government

Protector Somerset	-	Edward VI's chief adviser the 'good duke', whose lenient approach encouraged unrest, though he took a tougher line in July
Matthew Parker	-	Cambridge scholar, preached against the rebellion at Kett's camp and in St Clement's Church
Marquis of Northampton	-	commander of the first royal army defeated by the rebels on St Martin's Plain
Earl of Warwick	-	commander of the second royal army which defeated the rebels at Dussindale
Captain Drury	-	commander of a company of arquebusiers
Malatesta, Van Valderen and Hakefort	-	commanders of Italian, German and Imperial mercenaries used against the rebels

SOME STATISTICS OF THOSE WHO DIED DURING THE REBELLION

REBELS		GOVERNMENT FORCES	
Battle at Bishop Bridge, 22 July	20	Night attack and Battle on St Martin's Plain	20
Night attack, 31 July	300	Street fighting in Norwich	30
Battle on St Martin's Plain, 1 August	130	Battle of Dussindale	350
Executions in Norwich Market, 24 August	49	**TOTAL**	400
Street battles in Norwich, 24-25 August	330		
Battle of Dussindale, 27 August	3,000		
Executions after Dussindale	220		
TOTAL	4,049	All figures are approximate	

SOME OF KETT'S FOLLOWERS AND THEIR FATE

We know little about the thousands who followed Kett, but some light has been shed on the subject by a research project directed by Elizabeth Rutledge and Fiona Macdonald, which produced a list of 188 names of men known to have followed or sympathised with Kett. The list is a microcosm of the vast throng who were part of the Norfolk Rising, indicating home village, occupation and in many cases the involvement of these men in the Rebellion and their ultimate fate.

Nearly 50 different villages and towns are represented, evidence that Kett enjoyed support throughout most of Norfolk and that the Rebellion had urban as well as rural roots. Further, over 30 different occupations appear, from small farmers, artisans and tradesmen, to humble labourers. They include, yeoman, husbandman, butcher, parson, tailor, baker, weaver, carpenter, innkeeper, mariner, thatcher, hayer, boatwright, tanner, cordwainer, hatter, carrier, miller, cook, keelman, mercer, mason, smith, servant, fisherman, labourer and rat catcher.

The 49 men on the list who were pardoned, presumably benefited from Warwick's restraint after Dussindale (see page 64). Of these, 29 were imprisoned in Norwich, Yarmouth and King's Lynn and later released in March 1550. 16 were killed, six accused of 'seditious talk' and five were pilloried for the same offence.

Support and sympathy for Kett is revealed in various ways. For example, two men seized ammunition, one objected to Kett's hanging while another thought him an honest man. One threw Sir Roger Wodehouse in a ditch, one took information to the rebels, and the villagers of Heydon took a banner from their church to the rebel camp. Some pulled down fences or the pound, while others carried food and drink to the camp on Mousehold. Two men appeared before the Privy Council and there is a reminder of events in West Norfolk as one man visited the Downham Market camp and another was killed at Castle Rising.

CALENDAR OF PRINCIPAL EVENTS
IN KETT'S REBELLION
1549

JULY

6-7	The Wymondham Fair - grievances are aired
9	Kett leads a protest march against enclosure
12	Kett and his followers reach Mousehold Heath and set up a camp
14	Kett organises the camp from the Oak of Reformation, where gentry are brought for trial
15	Kett and his fellow 'Governors' send their 29 Requests for redress of grievances to the King
21	Kett rejects the pardon offered by Royal Herald; Norwich closes its gates to the rebel camp
22	Rebels force entry to Norwich via Bishop Bridge
31	Royal army commanded by Earl of Northampton arrives to suppress the rebels

AUGUST

1	Rebels defeat Northampton's force in battle on St Martin's Plain. Northampton retreats, leaving Norwich in Kett's hands
23	Warwick's army reaches outskirts of Norwich
24	Rebels reject pardon offered by Warwick's Herald, so royal soldiers break into Norwich; 49 rebels are captured and hanged
25	Fierce struggle for control of Norwich but rebels fail to drive Warwick out
26	Landnechts arrive and rebels break camp
27	Rebel army is defeated at Dussindale
28	Kett is captured at Swannington

SEPTEMBER

9	Kett is imprisoned in Tower of London

NOVEMBER

26	Robert &William Kett are found guilty of treason

DECEMBER

1	Kett is imprisoned in Norwich Guildhall dungeon
7	Kett is hanged at Norwich Castle and William from the west tower of Wymondham Abbey.

Select bibliography

I have consulted a wide variety of primary and secondary source material. The following have proved particularly useful.

Nicholas Sotherton	The Commoyson of Norfolk (c. 1560)
Alexander Neville	The Norfolk Furies (1575)
Holinshed	Chronicles (1578)
Blomefield	History Norfolk (1805-1810)
R. Davy	History of Rebellion in Norfolk
F.W. Russell	Kett's Rebellion in Norfolk (1859)
L.M. Kett	The Ketts of Norfolk (1921)
G. Kett	The Pedigree of Kett
S.K. Land	Kett's Rebellion (1977)
S.T. Bindoff	Tudor England (1950) Pelican
S.T. Bindoff	Ket's Rebellion (1949) Hist. Assn.
C.S.L. Davies	Peace, Print and Protestantism
J. Guy	Tudor England (1988)
G.R. Elton	England under the Tudors
D.M. Loades	Politics and the Nation (1974)
C. Hill	Reformation to Industrial Revolution
B. Robinson	Norfolk Mysteries Revisited (1996)
J. Clayton	Robert Kett & the Norfolk Rising
R. Groves	Rebel's Oak (1948)
W Rye	Depositions taken before mayor and aldermen of Norwich 1549-1567

An Historical Atlas of Norfolk - Norfolk Museums Service
T Chubb & G.A. Stephen - Descriptive List of the Printed Maps of Norfolk 1574-1916, and Descriptive List of Norwich Plans 1541-1914
City of Norwich Chamberlain's Accounts for 1549
Norfolk Archaeology, Volumes 9, 25, 26, 29 and 30
Norfolk Research Committee Bulletin Nos. 32 and33
Calendar of Patent Rolls 1547 - 1553